CW00762708

MY DARLING CHILDREN

It would finish me could I have taken a sprig of these brave men's laurels; they are, and I glory in them, my darling children, served in my school.

Lord Nelson in a letter to
Vice-Admiral Lord Keith,
Palermo, 8 April, 1800

MY DARLING CHILDREN

War From the Lower Deck

by
WILLIAM GRIFFITHS

with a Foreword by
Sir Michael Hordern
CBE

LEO COOPER
London

To the Professor with gratitude;
a gratitude which will not die until I do.

First published in Great Britain in 1992 by
LEO COOPER
190 Shaftesbury Avenue, London WC2H 8JL
an imprint of
Pen & Sword Books, Ltd,
47 Church Street, Barnsley, South Yorkshire S70 2AS

A CIP catalogue record for this book is available
from the British Library

ISBN: 0 85052 332 X

Typeset by Yorkshire Web, Barnsley, S. Yorks.
in Plantin 10 point

Printed by
Redwood Press,
Melksham, Wiltshire

CONTENTS

Let us not forget brave men and proud ships.

FOREWORD
by Sir Michael Hordern, CBE

Sometime matelot in the Fleet
of His Britannic Majesty.

It will bc notcd that cach chaptcr of this book is hcadcd by a quotation from the letters of an Admiral — Lord Nelson of immortal memory, but this is the background to the history of the war at sea written from the very heart of the lower deck, much of it in the splendidly inventive language of the messdecks; no asterisks and no apologies; that is the way it was. This is the real thing, the story of men who fought for their lives out upon the oceans; no 'screaming abdabs' from the film star 'survivors' in open boats in the tank at Pinewood Studios, but the reality of brave men and proud ships.

One weeps at 'there is no back door to a sinking ship' and one laughs like the proverbial Chief Stoker at the mad, e'en desperate, gaiety of their runs ashore in foreign parts with 'Knock-knock' Naylor, 'John O'Gaunt' and 'Smelly' Feates and their like, only to be jerked suddenly back into the violent and gulping actions off Crete, in the North Atlantic or on those horrific Russian convoys which this country, not to mention the Russians, should never be allowed to forget.

I share with the author convoy memories of screams of burnt and drowning men who, with the convoy at stake, one dared not stop to rescue. I am proud to remember that I was once Ordinary Seaman Hordern, M; a 'Guzz' (ex-Devonport) rating like the author of this book once was, and a contemporary of its heroes in HMS *Raleigh* and HMS *Drake* – Devonport Barracks – in 1940 where this book begins and where we learnt to respect, and to deride, those set in authority over us: from 'Gatey' Parsons, the Chief Gunnery Instructor, to the 'Jaunty' – Master-at-Arms – and e'en unto Their Lordships of Admiralty in their Legendary Wisdom.

With tears of nostalgia, the tenseness of excitement, and much laughter I found, as one who served for most of the war in HM Ships, this book to be unputdownable; for some days after reading it I was haunted by the spectres of 'Brave men and Proud Ships'; and that quotation would, I feel, have made a fitting title for this book; it certainly makes a fitting epitaph for those who went 'down to the sea in ships' in the Second World War and who never returned.

Michael Hordern
Chelsea, 1991

ACKNOWLEDGEMENTS

I would like to thank my long-suffering wife and all the men with whom I have been honoured and privileged to serve. I am also grateful to Leo Cooper, Tom Hartman and Beryl Hill for all their help and encouragement.

PROLOGUE

Friends, in and out of the Royal Navy, have told me that the human story of life at sea on the lower deck in the Second World War has yet to be written. Not having read all that has been written on the subject I am not qualified to judge; but, if that be true, then this is an inadequate attempt to tell that story, at least in part. No pen, and certainly not mine, will ever pay adequate tribute to the men who fought the war under the White Ensign. In this telling I am painting on a vast canvas, and I ask the reader to bear with obvious shortcomings.

This is not a history of the war at sea; it is the story behind the history; the story of the ordinary man in the street who went to sea to fight his country's battles; who, in most cases, did so with an unswerving faith in the justice of the cause for which he fought and, all too often, died. The men who fought the war at sea were no braver than the next man; they were brave because they had no choice. It was a case of fight or die; there is no back door to a sinking ship.

Unfashionable though it may be in this cynical age, this story waves the flag unashamedly, and I am sure that the men who found graves in the world's oceans would wish it no other way. This book is a tribute to them.

Every matelot who ever served the Royal Navy will recognize himself in these pages; but all the characters are fictitious, and bear no relation to any person living or dead. The characters here portrayed are composites, and bear much resemblance to many people, both living and dead – God bless 'em.

No apology is tendered for the language used; it is the language of the lower deck. Parts of this story may shock; but it is not designed to shock. This is a true story, and the truth is often shocking.

As all the events described actually happened, it has been found necessary to disguise the names of persons and ships, especially the ships in which the two main characters served; but the backcloth of war at sea has not been disguised — that remains forever true.

If I attempted to write this story in the language of the lower deck no one, other than a matelot, would understand it. Jack speaks a language all his own, honed and refined by centuries of usage, so where nautical terms and 'Navalese' are used I have made the meaning clear either in the text or in brackets; this, I feel, is preferable to a glossary.

In conclusion I must make it plain that this story was written in 1950 in an odd assortment of exercise books; the only thing that has happened to it since is that it has been typed and a prologue and epilogue added.

Chapter 1

War!

'It is, therefore, necessary that all good men should come forward on this momentous occasion to oppose the Enemy and, more particularly, the Sea-fencibles, who have voluntarily enrolled themselves to defend their country afloat, which is the true place where Britain ought to be defended, that the horrors of war may not reach the peaceful abodes of our families.'

Lord Nelson to Captains Shields, Hamilton, Schombergh and Edge.
6 August 1801.

'Right m'lads, get fell in over yer!'

The stentorian voice resounded throughout the station yard. The crowd of some two hundred or so young, and not so young, men who had just been disgorged from the Paddington to Plymouth train began to sort themselves into some semblance of good order until, by dint of much cajoling, they stretched the length of the station yard in two straggling and somewhat bewildered lines. The first time, but by no means the last, that they would obey that order.

'Keep silence, an' listen fer yer names!' bellowed the voice. 'When yew 'ears yer names called out take yer 'and baggage an' yew 'ops up inta the transport.'

One after another the recruits to the Naval service climbed into the waiting lorries. The operation was soon completed and the convoy moved off on what for all concerned was to prove the greatest adventure of their lives.

From all over the country the recruits had come – and from all walks of life. Some were called up for the duration of the war, others had volunteered for Naval service for a specific period on regular engagements. But, to a man, all were volunteers. At recruiting centres throughout the country the choice had been theirs; at this stage of the war the Royal Navy could still afford to cling to its volunteer tradition.

As the convoy threaded its way through the streets of Plymouth, necks were craned to catch glimpses of the ancient garrison town, this cradle of Britain's naval heritage; a heritage of which the recruits were not entirely unaware. Had not Sir Francis Drake played bowls on Plymouth Hoe? Even the name of the 'ship' to which they were bound was evocative of tradition and adventure upon the high seas; HMS *Raleigh*, the call-up notices said.

It was a novel experience for all, and there were among their number young men who had never in their lives left the confines of the city or town in which they had been born. One young man from Birmingham admitted that his first ever sight of the sea had been from the carriage windows of the train as it rounded Tor Bay on the journey down. For him, as for so many young men from time immemorial, the Royal Navy had offered escape from the narrow humdrum of everyday life.

The convoy turned into a gateway and rolled to a stop in front of a long, low building which was flanked by a vast expanse of no-man's-land, the parade ground. The latest recruits to the naval service had arrived aboard their first ship. They were the focus of all eyes.

Old salts from previous intakes and sailors of but a few weeks standing, hurled advice and insults at the latest influx: 'Go 'ome yew daft bastards! Go 'ome whilst ther's still time!'

The voice which at the station had greeted their arrival now came to their rescue, marshalled the New Entries – for as such they were now officially known – into straggling lines and marched them into the dining hall. Here they were confronted with an outsized meal – soup, main course and vegetables, and sweet, with unlimited scalding hot tea. It was a good meal by any standards and, perhaps for the only time in their naval careers, they were waited upon by the Duty Dining Hall Crew. The whole proceedings were presided over by a very fat and jovial Chief Petty Officer Cook, a veritable Friar Tuck of a man who regaled them with atrocious stories of the life upon which they were about to embark.

After the meal the New Entries were bidden to remain in the dining hall for a speech of welcome from the Training Commander, a tall distinguished-looking gent with gold lace around the sleeves of his reefer jacket and 'scrambled egg' on the peak of his cap. His audience gazed up in awe at the first, real naval officer many of them had ever seen. He stood tall and aloof upon a stage and gazed out upon the sea of upturned faces; a product of the Royal Naval College at Dartmouth and, from the age of thirteen, a lifetime spent at sea in many corners of the world. His voice, crisp and incisive, welcomed the recruits with few words and in unaffected tones. Briefly he outlined the pattern of their lives for the next six weeks and etched in a picture of the war at sea to date, asking them not to be lulled into a sense of false security by what he called the phoney war. There was nothing phoney, he assured them, about the battle of the oceans.

He concluded his speech of welcome by explaining the establishment's role as an induction centre which existed solely to provide basic training, square-bashing and elementary seamanship. For the most part they would complete their training elsewhere, according to the demands of the branch of the service for which they were selected, and taking into account any qualifications and previous experience.

From the dining hall the recruits were marched under the aegis of the voice – the owner of which became known, feared and respected under the name of 'Gatey' Parsons, chief gunnery and parade drill instructor – to the naval stores where each man was issued with a set of bedding, and from thence to the huts, or messdecks as they became known, which were to become their homes for the next six weeks.

At the messdecks, each man was allocated a bunk and a locker in which to put his possessions. Upon each bunk was a buff-coloured paper headed 'Next of Kin Form,' and beneath the spaces to be filled in 'in ink' there was written the ominous legend 'This is not a will; ratings wishing to make a will...' Nasty! It caused a lot of misgivings, and no little conjecture.

In the centre of the messdecks stoves were burning brightly, and around these the new entries gathered. The spring of 1940 being not too far advanced, there was yet a noticeable nip in the air and, after the events of the day, everyone felt the need of a little warmth, a little relaxation and a chance to take stock.

Soon, by the processes of natural selection, they gathered in small groups, each to his kind, and the messdecks filled with the babble of animated conversation; and, as the new entries relaxed and became better acquainted, peals of laughter and the horseplay borne of youthful exuberance became apparent.

Self-consciously they sized each other up, making mental reservations here, meeting a kindred spirit there; friends were made and aversions adopted. Writing materials appeared and a variety of books and papers made a tentative appearance, only to be discarded in favour of the topic uppermost in all their minds – the Navy and the war.

Apart from the air raid precautions, with the blackout and its irksome restrictions, the war seemed very remote, and the war at sea even more so. To date the seriousness of the situation had not permeated the majority of the British public. The war was at that stage of unreality which preceded Dunkirk, the repercussions of which were shortly to shatter the illusions of a people who, ostrich like, hid their heads in the sand of gullibility and pinned their faith in that surprisingly large, horoscopic section of the national press which predicted an end to hostilities before Christmas.

The Royal Navy, fulfilling its traditional role as the nation's first line of defence, had been at war since the day war was declared, indeed since that day in September, 1939, when SS *Athenia* had been sunk by a U-boat in the North Atlantic and the war at sea had become a grim reality.

Even now, as the New Entries sat before the messdeck stoves, convoys crawled the world's shipping lanes to which U-boats clung like leeches. Day and night without let up hunter and hunted played a deadly game of oceanic hide-and-seek, and shipping losses mounted by the hour.

There was plenty for the New Entries to talk about, and talk they did until, suddenly, and without so much as a by-your-leave, another raucous voice intruded into their lives. The hubbub of the messdecks hushed at its command, and doors and windows shook at the verbal blast. A Petty Officer had entered, belted and gaitered and, with a terrible voice, demanded: 'Silence in the mess.'

Silence reigned, despotic and absolute. In a broad West Country accent Petty Officer 'Pincher' Martin introduced himself as their instructor. Fat, short and normally jovial, with a nose which denoted over-indulgence in Nelson's blood (rum), he stood, arms akimbo, and briefly outlined the programme for the remainder of the day. This consisted mainly of supper and its aftermath. He then dealt with the following day's routine in greater detail, glowered around the assembled company and left, switching on the tannoy as he did so, and leaving in his wake a further chatter of speculation. This speculation was suddenly stilled by the insistent blare of a bugle announcing supper.

The meal was followed by a move back to the messdecks, where preparations were made for sleep; this was the ritual which became variously known as 'crashing the swede' (head), 'hitting the sack,' 'floggin' the pit,' 'turning in,' and ' 'oppin' aboard the aerial sofa' (hammock).

At ten o'clock the noise of the messdecks was again hushed, this time by a strange whistling noise which emanated from the loudspeakers and sounded, someone said, 'like a bleedin' budgerigar on heat.' But 'twas not 'a bleedin' dicky bird,' merely the Bosun's Mate trilling on his pipe (whistle) and announcing to the nautical world at large that it was the end of another day. It was time to 'pipe down' and go to bed.

Five minutes later Petty Officer Martin reappeared, chased the stragglers off to bed, wished them a collective goodnight and switched off the lights before leaving to retire to bed with, it was rumoured, a bottle of rum for a bedmate.

*

On the messdecks the silence of the early morning was disturbed only by the occasional grunt and the sound of heavy breathing when, suddenly, and without the slightest warning, the quiet was rent asunder by the imperative notes of the bugle as it sounded 'Wakey-Wakey'. No sooner had the latest demanding note died away than Petty Officer Martin reappeared. Gone was his affability of the previous night; here was a different 'Pincher' indeed. His rotund and animated figure stomped up and down the messdecks and, in a voice which sounded like a file on galvanized iron, he exhorted everyone to ' 'op out!' and, as the reluctance of his charges became apparent, he waxed even more insistent:

' 'op out, yew idle bastards,' he roared, ' 'it the poxy deck!'

The sleepy-eyed New Entries ' 'it the poxy deck' and, under the critical surveillance of his somewhat jaundiced eye, donned singlets and trousers, grabbed toilet gear, and ran shivering to the washrooms; from there to finish dressing, make their bunks, and march to the dining hall for breakfast – bacon and train smash (bacon and tomatoes). Afterwards they returned to the messdecks to, as 'Pincher' put it, stow gear, give it a 'chamfer-up,' and leave things all shipshape and Bristol fashion.

Then they were marched to the parade ground where they were divided into classes of thirty with a Class Leader appointed by Chief Petty Officer 'Gatey' Parsons.

From the parade ground they went to the sick bay. Here everyone, except the medicos of course, ran around stark naked and suffered the most searching and undignified scrutiny. It is difficult to retain one's dignity when one's private part is being lifted at the end of a pencil and scrutinized as if it was some form of malignant growth, and when one then has a suitably vaselined finger shoved up one's rectum.

From medical inspection they moved on to personnel selection. They emerged as Seamen, Stokers, Signalmen, Cooks, Stewards, Stores Assistants ('Jack Dusties'), Writers, and a dozen other branches that catered for the demands of the highly complex modern fleet.

Upon completion of the induction ceremony the newly categorized classes were marched to the kitting-up store, here to be issued with the numerous items which comprise the sailor's kit. Firstly a kit bag in which to put everything; then boots, socks, underwear, uniforms, caps, overcoat, oilskin, cap tally, a collection of brushes for many purposes, and a variety of other items.

From the kitting-up store they went to the messdecks, there to be initiated under the bibulous tutelage of Petty Officer Martin into the mysteries of tape and flap, dicky front, and tiddly bow, and there to don the uniform of His Britannic Majesty's Royal Navy and to fold away civilian clothes before their despatch home.

By dint of much swapping and helpful advice from the by now very mellow Pincher – it being after tot time – everyone achieved something like a reasonable fit. The mysteries and potential of the trouser flap were explained, tapes and collars were mastered, silks folded 'proper pusser' (in service-like manner); a wide assortment of bows appeared on HMS cap tallies, and caps were pulled, twisted, kicked and jumped upon, and generally abused until something like a salty looking fit was obtained.

Eventually three fairly orderly ranks of comparatively well-dressed sailors-to-be fell in on the parade ground at three-thirty that afternoon where they were told that the time was not three-thirty, but fifteen thirty – 'an' no bloody howers on the end!' All very nautical. 'Gatey' Parsons ran a practised eye over the assembly. They looked raw and awkward in their brand-new and not-too-well-fitting suits, but a few visits to the tailor's shop and six weeks under his tutelage would soon put all to rights. They also had yet to be inveigled into buying a tiddly suit – a best suit obtained from non-service sources, and not quite conforming to regulation pattern – and beguiled into the sartorial parlours of the naval tailors of Devonport, there to be outfitted with all those items of apparel so dear to the well-dressed sailor's heart – bell-bottomed trousers that really were belled, sky-blue collars, gold-wire cap-tallies, and silks with a sheen akin to the polish on a whore's bum. All those things in fact which proclaim a man a real salt, a proper Jack m'hearty – and all for a few bob a week.

Meanwhile it was 'Gatey' Parsons' job to shake the rawness out of these men, which he did without delay. Within a month or two they would be at sea. In the six weeks at his disposal he had to mould them into something resembling sailors, teach them a new set of values, teach them immediate reaction and unquestioning obedience to orders, and instil into them the meaning of team spirit, and generally make them fit to take their place alongside the men already serving the Fleet.

'Gatey' had one particularly personal way of putting across a point, strictly for the New Entries' private ear, and not to be bawled across the parade ground. 'It maight hoffend the delicate ears of hofficers wot maight be listening.' Breathing sweet nothings down the luckless recruit's ear he was wont to murmur, 'An' when I sez jump me lad I means JUMP, an' yew don't bleedin' well come down 'til I tells ya! Now bleedin' JUMP!' And jump they did.

The Navy was short of escorts and the men to man them; convoy commitments were exorbitant in both. The bigger ships of the line, the battleships, cruisers, aircraft carriers, and depot ships, were also crying out for men. With the fitting of the greater fire power demanded by war, and the introduction of more sophisticated equipment in modern ships, the Navy's manpower was stretched to the limit; and here, on this parade ground, were some of the men who within weeks would be manning those ships. At sea their lives would depend upon the lessons learned on this parade ground under the eagle-eyed and stentorian-voiced 'Gatey' Parsons and his minions. They would give of their best because there was just no other way. There is no back door to a sinking ship.

'Gatey' was fully aware of his responsibilities and knew what was required of him and why. He was a man who from his boy's service in HMS *Ganges*, had given a lifetime's service. He had grown old in the Navy, and was steeped in its ways and its traditions.

Six feet two inches in height and stiff of back, with features which looked as if they had been chiselled from the granite of his native Cornwall, his youthful figure and bearing belied his fifty summers. A martinet and disciplinarian of the old school, a man to be feared, his lips could yet curl into a friendly grin, and the crow's feet at the corners of his eyes pucker with good humour. But that voice, that dreadful voice! From a comfortable job as a commissionaire in a Truro bank he had been brought back to the service by the war to make sailors out of the nondescript influx from the recruiting offices. And make sailors he would, or know the reason why.

Day after weary day they marched and drilled, with and without rifles. They learned how to salute, with the palm of the hand facing downwards, 'Hofficers don't laik ta see saylars' dirty paws,' and how to take off their caps in three distinct movements, by numbers, 'Hup-two-three-down'. They boxed the compass, steered a dummy ship, swung the lead, in more ways than that shown in the Manual of Seamanship, tied knots, spliced ropes and wires, learned the difference between a length of cable and a cable's length, between bollard and fairlead, and capstan and winch. Left, looking for'ard towards the 'sharp end' of the ship, became port, and right, looking in the same direction, became starboard – 'an' don't ferget to reverse it when yew'm lookin' in the hopposite direction!' Floors were transmogrified into decks, walls into bulkheads, ceilings into deckheads, and the lavatory became the heads. When leaving the establishment they no longer went out, but ashore, or over the prow. The Main Gate assumed a new significance as the gangway, usually referred to as the gangplank, with its approach on the inboard, or establishment side, known and sanctified as the holy of holies: the Quarterdeck.

After six weeks of intensive training they were fitter than they had ever been in their lives, and, in all probability, ever would be again, especially after they had been at sea for a few months living in the cramped and stuffy atmosphere of a man o' war's 'tween decks under wartime conditions of black-out, closed port holes, and battened-down hatches.

Came the day of the final parade, the day that each and everyone had longed for. They stood on the parade ground, fully rigged, victualled and watered, and in all respects ready for sea, listening to the Captain's speech of farewell.

He complimented them on their conduct and achievements under training. They were to be given a long weekend leave and, on their return, would join Royal Naval Barracks, Devonport, and from there they would be dispersed to active service with the Fleet.

Chapter 2

One of the 'Tribals'

'To me it is perfectly indifferent to what quarter of the world we go: with a good Ship and a good Ship's company we can come to no harm.'
Captain Horatio Nelson to the Reverend William Nelson. August, 1787.

The Royal Naval Barracks, Devonport, a grey-stoned, sombre citadel, built next to the Royal Naval Dockyard has since it was built ever been the site of every pernicious imposition Their Lordships of Admiralty – in their legendary wisdom – have visited upon poor luckless sailors.

Ordinary Seaman John William Thomas and his friend the 'Professor', otherwise Ordinary Seaman Walter Pater Martin-Smith, were no exceptions as they queued outside the DFDO (Detailed for Draft Office). They had left basic training in HMS *Raleigh* two weeks before, and after a long weekend leave and two weeks' sculling about in barracks, they were now Detailed for Draft to a ship, or to wherever Their Lordships felt disposed to send them; hence their presence in the queue outside that oracular consulting room, that place of men's destiny, the Drafting Office.

For the hundredth time the Professor enquired: 'Wonder where they are sending us, Johnny?' and for the hundredth time he received the same reply: 'Christ knows, your guess is as good as mine Prof; prob'ly some filfy 'ole like Freetown or the Persian Gulf.'

'Anywhere,' replied his friend, 'is better than this rotten grot (grotto).

' 'Ere 'ave a tickler' (home-made cigarette). Thomas passed the makings and, in a manner which would have done credit to any three badge AB (long service Able Seaman), they rolled cigarettes deftly between their fingers.

A few days earlier the Luftwaffe had dropped bombs on East Anglia, and the Professor was anxious about his parents back home in London. He voiced the thought which was uppermost in his mind at the moment: 'Reckon they'll bomb London?' and he looked to his friend for reassurance.

'Not on your nelly... Air Force'll stop 'em.'

There was little conviction in his words despite his optimism for the sake of his friend. He knew, as all the nation knew, that it was but a matter of time before Adolf Hitler carried out his threat to raze the British capital to the ground. *Blitzkreig*, or something, he called it.

They were an oddly assorted pair, the Professor and Thomas, but between them there was growing a very real bond of friendship. The Professor was tall, angular, and lean of feature, with a fine passionate mouth and quick intelligent eyes which viewed the world from beneath a permanently furrowed brow. Life for him was a huge question mark, and something which could never be reduced to simple terms. Scholarship had taken him to London University via the local grammar school. In London he had had to work to maintain himself and his studies and, after gaining his Ph.D (Econ.), he worked and lectured. Big words rolled off his tongue as easily as water off a hatch coaming; he had a propensity for the high-flown phrase, and liked to hear himself talk; he was a teacher.

Most of his messmates treated him with amused tolerance; just the man to help a chap out with the *Daily Mirror* crossword puzzle, but not a man to take too seriously. Friendship apart, the relationship between him and Johnny Thomas was in the nature of teacher and taught. The Professor talked and Thomas listened and asked questions. They often lay, hammocks slung side by side in the darkness of the messdecks, and talked well into the night, mulling over the problems which beset mankind. The classics would be quoted, flights of poetic fancy indulged, and the conversation would shoot off on the widest tangents to cover every field of human endeavour.

These nocturnal tête-à-têtes were invariably terminated by a well-aimed boot, and a wrathful 'Pipe down yew bastards!' from a sleep-courting messmate.

'Stripey' Winterbottom (so called because of his three Good Conduct Badges, denoting, according to Service lore, twelve years of undetected crime) had called the Professor's nickname into being. In reply to a question arising from a purely academic discussion on whether a man, as epitomized by the Naval branch of the species *Homo sapiens*, could legitimately commit adultery whilst away from home in pursuit of affairs Naval, and yet condemn his wife for doing the same thing in his absence, he had replied: 'Fucked if I know; ask the bleedin' Professor over there!'

So the Professor was asked, and christened; and so it would ever remain; nicknames die hard in the Navy.

At last came the turn of Thomas and the Professor at the Drafting Office window.

'Name?' The voice of the invisible dispenser of draft chits answered its own question.

'Martin... blimey!.. bloody hayphen ...Smiff!'

'Official number?'

'Mess?'

'Thomas, John... Jesus!.. 'oo ever christened yew 'ad a sense of 'umour... whadda they call yew... pricky?.. Ha ha ha... Official number?.. Mess?'

'You'm goin' ta *Caucasian* Martin-Smiff, yew too, Thomas!' barked the voice. 'Join 'er at Liverpool day atter tomorra,' and two draft chits were handed out of the window.

'Gityerbaganammickpackedandgitbackyersharpish!'

'What is she?' in reply to a query from Thomas. Such abysmal ignorance brought an indignant nose poking through the window: 'Whaddaya fink 'tis... a bleedin' carley float?.. a bleedin' ship uv course... destroyer... one uv the Tribals... 14th Flotilla... now piss off!'

The nose twitched with indignation at the temerity of the character who had the audacity to ask what it was to which he was being sent – as if it was any of his business where the clown was going! Time enough to worry about that when he got there.

The routine medical, dental, naval stores, and all the other departments necessary for a man on draft to visit and get the all-important rubber stamp, was quickly done, kitbags were packed and next morning, in company with a dozen or so other ratings, Johnny Thomas and the Professor found themselves on the 0900 train, northbound to the land of Scouse and raunchy barmaids; that, anyway, was the way Liverpool was described to them.

The train was packed with a heterogeneous representation of wartime travellers; but, being a naval draft, theirs was a reserved compartment, and they soon settled into the boredom of the long journey, via Exeter, Bristol, Worcester and Crewe.

Hour after weary hour the train steamed north. In the barracks speculation had been rife concerning *Caucasian*, but there are few secrets in the Navy; it had been learned that she was one of the destroyers operating from Scapa Flow with the Home Fleet escort force. All were named after tribes; *Caucasian* was one of the Tribals.

These ships were the Navy's latest and finest destroyers, they ranked among the fastest ships in the world, were built like small cruisers and, with armament to match their speed, were a match for anything of comparable size afloat. They were the spearhead of the fleet's striking power, and were to find action and to prove their worth times out of number. If there was a tricky job to do it was, so often, the Tribals which did it. Their history became the history of the war at sea, and few of them survived to see the return of peace.

As the new members of her company were being hurried north *Caucasian* was in the dock repairing damage sustained in support of *Warspite* at Narvik, where Captain Warburton-Lee won his posthumous Victoria Cross in *Hardy*. She was also giving a few days' well-earned leave to her ship's company. A rare luxury.

Caucasian had buried her dead at sea. The German shell which had ripped through her superstructure had taken its toll of life, and the northbound draft were replacements for her dead.

These were things the draft were to learn. Meanwhile conversation had lapsed in the compartment, the monotony of the journey had lulled most of its occupants to an uneasy train-journey sleep; others read or gazed pensively out of the compartment window.

A general re-awakening heralded their arrival at Liverpool. In the station yard lorries were waiting to take the draft to the docks. A local lad, excited at the prospect of seeing Mum again, acted as guide to his home town and pointed out places of interest; the towering mass of the Liver Building, shortly to become the headquarters of the newly formed Western Approaches Command; the Birkenhead ferry and the Mersey with its mighty concourse of shipping of all nations, both merchant and Royal Navy; from ocean liners, drab and anonymous now in their uniform of wartime grey, to dirty, rusted and unpretentious coastal tramps, and the sleek graceful lines of the destroyers and cruisers fresh from the builders' yards or just returned from, or going out to, the ocean battlefields.

Fussy little tugs went about the business of the great river; pushing, pulling, nudging and hooting, they churned the waters into mud-and-oil-fouled foam as they shepherded the heavily-laden cargo vessels alongside the docks, or swung them out into the river for passage downstream to the convoy rendezvous and the world's seaways.

The destroyers which would escort these ships upon their ocean journeys fussed around; sleek, not always well groomed, but efficient, they lifted their skirts, hooted disdainfully, and swept off down river unaided. 'Hurry along there!' they seemed to say 'We'll wait for you down at the bar,' and off they went, to plunge once more into the vortex of the Atlantic convoy battles.

The lorries rolled to a halt on the Gladstone Dock. In the dock lay an oddly assorted collection of warships, mostly escort vessels; corvettes, sloops, minesweepers, and destroyers, and a cruiser fitting out after leaving the builder's yard. Every inch of wall space was full. Ships of all shapes and sizes.

From the gangway of *Caucasian* came a raucous shout of welcome: 'Come aboard, yew lucky bastards, come aboard!'

The vociferous Able Seaman who rejoiced in the office of Boatswain's Mate had shouted this time-honoured greeting with a grin which split his freckled face from ear to ear and, as the new arrivals humped their bags and hammocks over the gangway, he began in broad West Country accents to regale them with heart-rending stories of life aboard this 'orphanated pig's bastard'. According to his account *Caucasian* rolled 'like a fuckin' baff tub in a tornader, smelt like a Maltese drain, and leaked like a bleedin' collander wiv a 'ole in it'. Her Captain had been spawned from some Goanese brothel; all the officers – with the exception of 'Navvy' (the Navigating Officer), whom he accounted his chum – sprang from even more dubious origins, for the most part unspecified; 'an' as fer that louse-bound git the Coxun,' well, he defeated even Able Seaman 'Sludge' Coles's defamatory prowess.

'Sludge,' the proud possessor of the Distinguished Service Medal, was twenty years of age; in experience he was a hundred. To anyone prepared to listen he was prepared to tell *ad infinitum* how he sank the German Fleet single-handed. His freckles and tousled ginger hair, atop which sat a somewhat decrepit-looking stormy weather seaman's cap, gave him a schoolboyish look. This illusion, however, was soon dispelled when 'Sludge' opened his mouth; he possessed the most extensive, blasphemous vocabulary, and could – so he claimed – cuss for ten minutes flat without stopping to draw breath, or using the same word twice. 'Sludge' was very much the Jack m'hearty; a man of parts indeed. In five years' service, since the age of fifteen, he had sailed around the world in the Boys' Mess of HMS *Hood*, and fought in three major Fleet actions; two in northern waters in his present ship, and in the Battle of the River Plate in HMS *Exeter*. Everyone liked 'Sludge,' despite the fact that he suffered from what the Professor called the twin diseases of cussitus and dripsomania – he simply could not stop dripping (complaining).

Caucasian's Coxswain, Chief Petty Officer Torpedo Gunner's Mate Albert George Rothwell DSM, was found in the cubbyhole which rejoiced in the rather grandiose title of 'Ship's Office'. Here there was barely sufficient room to stow a kitbag and, oblivious to the world about him the swine ('swain) was wrestling with that iniquitous imposition of Their Lordships – known as the 'victualled and checked returns' for the quarter just ended; for the successful fiddling of which, he contended, he needed occult powers and a mind like a bleedin' adding machine.

Obviously, he was not a man who suffered an idiotic matelot gladly. He was not possessed of the milk of human kindness; and, allied to a meticulous eye for detail, he possessed a quick and scathing wit. He was the most hated man on the ship, and he did not give a damn about that. He, despite anything ever heard to the contrary, invented that phantom sailor 'Kilroy' – 'Kilroy wus 'ere, Kilroy wus there, Kilroy strikes again!' Anything that went wrong, and there was no one upon whom the blame could be pinned, it was always 'Kilroy's' fault. So CPO Rothwell was always referred to as 'Kilroy'.

As soon as those worthy adjuncts to the Navy, Thomas and the Professor, poked their noses around the office door he told the former to get his bloody hair cut, and the latter to get his suit pressed – sharpish.

Kilroy never smiled; or, if he did, he did it in his hammock when nobody was looking. He was a disciplinarian, as well he might be, being the senior lower-decker in a Fleet destroyer with some two hundred or so men on his 'slop-chit'. Matelots are up to all the tricks in the book, and a few which aren't; he needed to be hard, and hard he was. He had grown up in hard days; days when life in the Royal Navy was a highly desirable alternative to the dole queue and a home denuded by poverty and the means test. The only pair of boots he had ever possessed before joining the Navy – so he said – had been given to him by conscience-ridden charity, and these had been worn down to the uppers when, little more than a boy, he had joined the hungry and workless on their migration to London. Here, with the aid of a working man's hostel, he had eked out a living until he had joined the Navy. He was a bread-and-butter sailor, and had risen to the top of his chosen profession in the days when merit, not necessity, had governed the rate of promotion. The pre-war Navy had been no sinecure, and he had attained the dizzy heights at a very early age; when promoted to Chief Petty Officer he had not yet completed his first twelve years' service, an achievement almost unheard of in those days.

Slim and of medium height, with jet-black hair sleekly groomed and dark of visage, he wore his badge of office with complete authority and confidence in his own ability. He was an ambitious man, a candidate for Warrant Officer and, ultimately, Lieutenant, and he made no secret of the fact that he intended to reach the top – as far as any lower-decker could go in those days – and God help any man who got in his way. The lower deck of *Caucasian* reckoned that he would shop 'is dad, or sell 'is grandma up the creek. Not a man in the ship was not of the opinion that he was an absolute, unadulterated bastard.

Thomas and the Professor could know none of these things as they stood in the Ship's Office; but they sensed the presence of the master and trod a wary path in their first encounter with the man who, to all intents and purposes, really ran the ship, and ruled it with a rod of iron.

Joining formalities completed, the Coxswain sent them on their way to the for'ard messdeck which was to become their home for months to come. Everywhere was austerity and fighting equipment and not an inch of wasted space. Here was an atmosphere of potency and power leashed, and here also was character. All ships have character and no sailor ever forgets his first ship.

Nearly every member of the ship's company was ashore on leave; either all night leave, or the few days granted to each watch whilst the ship was undergoing repairs. *Caucasian* was almost empty.

The messdecks were small, and appeared even smaller than they actually were because of the amount of space given over to hammock stowage and lockers. Overhead was a mass of pipes; electrical conduits, ventilator trunking, ammunition hoists and hammock bars. Between the hammock bars were slung empty hammocks because it was the custom to sling a messmate's hammock in readiness for his return from shore; or, if he went ashore at a late enough hour, he would sling it himself. A wise precaution indeed when consideration is given to the lateness of the hour, and the condition to which sailors are prone on return from their nocturnal revelries.

Under the friendly guidance of the 'Killick of the Mess' (Leading Seaman in Charge) the new boys settled in, unpacked their kitbags, slung their hammocks in readiness for the night, and did full justice to the suppers which had been kept for them.

In the days ahead the Killick of the Mess, Leading Seaman 'Darby' Allen, would become their friend, tutor, protector, sea-daddy, and father confessor. Quietly, and without undue verbosity, he put them in the picture and, as he talked, he stitched away diligently at his embroidery. Darby was making a bedspread for his wife; all flowers and frills, and beautifully executed on a large square of pure silk which he had brought from Hong Kong just before war started. It was mooted in the mess that 'Darby'll get a tater or two fer that when he gets it 'ome!' (Tater – sexual intercourse). Delicately and beautifully stitched, a lot of Darby's soul was in that embroidery; it was a labour of love; love of Mrs Allen.

0630 the following morning and the slumbering, snoring, grunting stillness of just before the awakening was suddenly shattered by the rude intrusion of that virtuoso of the Bo'sun's Call, that butcher of the spoken word, 'Sludge' Coles.

'Wakey... wakey... wakey... rise an' shine!.. up yew gets yew showera... good fer nuffink bastards... come away yew drunken bums... come away me 'earty tars... come away, come away, come away!... this is the day we goes ta sea, yew lucky bastards!..; wakey, wakey, wakey!... rise an' shine me 'earty tars!' Followed by more trills on the pipe, and more verbal contributions to his seemingly purely personal desire to see 'Yew idle gits 'it the bleedin' deck!' He then proceeded to give his friends – he had no enemies – a personal shake by thumping hammocks and shouting exhortations to ' 'op out, Mick... shake 'alf way down, Jan boy?' or 'C'mon, Jock, yew 'eathen haggis yaffling Scotch git, 'op out!'

Many there were who had no need to lash hammocks; they had not slept in them. When they had staggered back aboard in the early hours they had been in no fit state to crawl into a 'mick' (hammock); they had merely crashed (slept) on the nearest table or bench, or curled up in the first corner they fell into.

The hangovers were monumental.

The messdecks, empty the night before, were now crowded. The ship's company had been arriving back all through the night; some had returned subdued, quietly, their thoughts still at home with the family. Others came boisterous from the fleshpots of Liverpool, after having been thrown out of the pubs in town and those near the docks; with the instincts of homing pigeons, they had staggered back to their ship. Others still were in no fit state to get back under their own steam; being unable to walk they had to be carried back by helpful shipmates, often in little better shape, to be dumped on benches or stowed away under tables to sleep the sleep of over-indulgence.

There had, of course, been the odd fight or two. What was a run ashore without a touch of the ol' fisticuffs? One or two black eyes were proudly flaunted to admiring messmates as their owners emerged from beneath tables and out of corners to view the new day with bloodshot and jaundiced eyes. Slowly, and with reluctance, the hands restored to life; black and jaundiced of eye, fatheaded, reeking of beer and spew, and with the mud of Liverpool's gutters and the sawdust of many a pub about their uniforms, they went about the business of preparing the ship for sea. But despite all, or perhaps because of all, everyone agreed that it had been 'a bloody good run ashore', the memories of which would sustain them in the hard days which lay ahead – and until the next time, if there ever was a next time.

The Professor dressed and lashed his hammock and, as he did so, he felt he could detect undercurrents of tension, perhaps an air of apprehension; nothing tangible, just a feeling, something hidden. A lot of the humour seemed forced; these messmates of his were hiding their true feelings about going back to Scapa Flow. He was jerked back to the present by the enraged howl of a messmate who was hopping around in the nude.

'Some dirty thievin' bastard, some lousy sex maniac, 'as thieved me knicks!' he howled. 'Of all the dirty, rotten moves... me fuckin' underpants 'as bin stole!'

Caucasian was on the canteen messing system whereby the ship's company were fed in their messes because there was no room for a dining hall in a destroyer, as opposed to the centralized messing system where everyone is fed in a dining hall under the auspices of a pay officer. Under the canteen messing system messes do their own catering, and such food as they eat is paid for by an allowance from the Admiralty. Anything consumed over this allowance is paid for, in the form of a monthly mess bill, by the messes themselves, the cost of which is shared equally amongst members of the mess. If, however, the mess does not take up its full allowance the resultant profit is shared out. The Seamen's Mess in *Caucasian*, wherein now lived Johnny Thomas and the Professor, was in debt to Their Lordships, so breakfast was a mere formality, and consisted of a cup of tea and a Woodbine. As Able Seaman 'Sludge' Coles said, 'the bloody war is being fought by Joe bleedin' Lyons and W.D & H.O. fuckin' Wills!'

At 0815 the ship's company was mustered 'Part of Ship' on the upper deck – that section of the ship to which each man was assigned – to be detailed off for the day's work. In less than two hours the ship was required to slip and proceed to sea, but before she could be cleared away there was plenty to do, and that which was not done could be left to the 'shake down' period on passage to Scapa Flow. The main task now was to get her squared away, off the wall, and down river.

To the assembled ship's company the Captain spoke a few words; welcomed new faces, expressed hopes for the future, and congratulated everyone on their exemplary behaviour whilst in Liverpool! Commander Philip St John Norton DSO, DSC, RN, was aloof, impartial, scrupulously fair in all his dealings and, as befits a destroyer captain, a trifle mad. Not one man present on that day when *Caucasian* put back to sea would not have cheerfully followed him to the ends of the earth – or up a Norwegian fjord. From the age of thirteen he had served his country; from Dartmouth as a cadet to his present command his life had been dedicated to the Royal Navy; he knew no other way of life. With very little money behind him, and a long line of ancestors who had served the Navy, his main assets were his ability as a seaman and as a Naval Officer, and he excelled at both.

It would be no exaggeration to say that the ship's company worshipped their Captain, he was a rare breed of man, and he in turn respected his ship's company, and the result was a happy ship.

As the ship's company dispersed about the business of preparing the ship for sea the First Lieutenant made an aside to his Captain to the effect that, by the looks of things, Liverpool had received a fresh coat of red paint the previous night.

'That, Number One' the Captain had replied, 'is how it should be; I would have been perturbed had it been otherwise... we all needed to clean our boilers; a few days at sea will blow away the cobwebs.'

'Fore part for'ard, after part aft, hands to stations for leaving harbour; special sea dutymen close up,' and the pipe trilled again.

From the bridge:

'Let go for'ard.'

'All gone for'ard, Sir!'

'Let go aft.'

'All gone aft, Sir!'

The engine room telegraph rang for 'slow ahead, starboard engine,' and *Caucasian* began to move slowly off the wall. On the bridge the Captain squinted into the early sun, scanned the basin, scanned the exit, and looked up and down the river. Fore and aft, above and below decks, the hands secured for sea. In the engine room the Chief Engine Room Artificer watched the telegraph repeater, and the Engineer Officer listened to the rising voice of his engines. He need not have worried, the dockyard had done their work well, and his charges responded beautifully to the opening throttle.

The telegraph rang down for 'slow astern port engine'; the 'old man' was swinging the ship in mid-basin, to point her nose through the exit and down river. Her screws churned the muddy waters of the basin to a dirty brown foam, then came the order 'slow ahead, both engines,' and *Caucasian* was on her way down to the Mersey Bar and the open sea. With the White Ensign fluttering proudly from the jack-staff, bunting fluttering from her yards, and the thumpity-thumpity-thump of her engines sounding like some rhythmic tribal war chant, she looked, and was, a proud ship; and, on this day in the early summer of 1940 as she returned to the battlefield of the northern ocean, her only farewell was the ragged cheer raised by the watching dockyard maties and the occasional shout from the shore. Her true farewells were being said in the hearts of her company, and in the hearts of those whose only recourse was to wait at home.

The Mersey Bar was cleared, the hands went to cruising stations, the watches were set, and the ship's rakish bows were pointed north-about through the Irish Sea, the North Channel and the Minches to Scapa Flow.

Chapter 3

Work Up

'I believe we are in the right fighting trim, let them come as soon as they please. I never saw a Fleet altogether so well officered and manned.'
Vice Admiral Lord Nelson to Alexander Davison Esq. 4 October, 1803.

The term 'evolutions' is common enough in the Royal Navy, yet its very mention is enough to make the stoutest matelot's heart shrink with apprehension. It is a term beloved of Commanding Officers and Officers of Flag Rank (Admirals) and can best be described as a series of exercises designed, with diabolical ingenuity, to 'work up' a ship and its company to full fighting efficiency, ready to meet any exigency and, having reached that desirable state, to keep it that way. Evolutions may take place at any hour of the day or night without the slightest warning or as much as a 'by your leave,' and are conducted in strict conformity with the King's Regulations and Admiralty Instructions, Admiralty Fleet Orders, The Manual of Naval Warfare, the Manual of Seamanship, all subsequent amendments to the foregoing, not forgetting precedent – with and without – and naval tradition. The only publications not consulted are the Bill of Rights, the Charter for the Prevention of Cruelty to Sailors and the Holy Bible. The subtlety employed has a touch of the Machiavellian; indeed, a touch of the sadistic and even of the corrupt. Able Seaman 'Sludge' Coles summed it all up when the first 'Evolutions Acquaint' was promulgated. 'T'ain't bleedin' nat'ral,' he said. 'Ther' oughta be a bleedin' law agin it... 'Snother uv they cases uv man's bleedin' in'umanity to man!'

Caucasian and HMS *Bulldog* ('ol' slobbery snout') with whom she had rendezvoused off the Mull of Kintyre, ran the whole gamut of evolutions as, in company, they steamed north. They towed aft, towed for'ard, went to action stations 'at the rush' at dawn, at dusk, and in the middle of the night, at 'tot time' – very popular move that! – and in the middle of dinner. Depth charges were transferred to *Bulldog* by light jackstay, and the Captain was rowed across to the 'chummy ship' by whaler to take lunch with his opposite number – 'pull yew lazy showera loafin' bastards, pull!' And the Coxswain fell out of the boat. *Caucasian*'s Medical Officer was also sent across on the jackstay, and he entered into the spirit of the thing by returning a luckless Steward, supposedly wounded in action, strapped in a *Neil Robertson* stretcher; and, as the two ships rolled toward each other at the same moment, the poor steward was nearly drowned.

Caucasian's ship's company were called upon to perform the most unusual duties. The Leading Sick Berth Attendant, Leslie (otherwise Ivor) Payne, was detailed to rescue the Chief Stoker from where he lay mortally wounded upon the engine room catwalk; and as the Chief of all the Stokers was raised through the engine room hatch strapped in a *Neil Robertson* stretcher – all eighteen stone of him – the air was fouled with blasphemy as 'Chiefy' got stuck in the hatch. The Canteen Damager (Manager) was ordered to convey six rounds of 4.7 ammunition from the for'ard magazine to the after gun position where, to the vociferous indignation of every 'shitehawk' (seagull) in the Western Isles, it was fired off in quick succession. Thomas Mancroft, Petty Officer Steward, was taxed to the limits of his ingenuity to provide a meal, alfresco, on the bridge for the Captain and six officers in five minutes flat; he then with the aid of the Cooks of the galley staff fed the ship's company an action messing dinner of corned beef and mashed potatoes in about the same time. The engine room was hit by an enemy shell and caught fire. The 'fire' was brought under control by the Chief Stoker and his minions, after the Chief had been released from the confines of the *Neil Robertson* by the 'chancre bosun' (Sick Berth Attendant). As if these impositions were not enough the after watertight bulkhead had to go and cave in and the air was again befouled by the language of the Chief of all the Stokers as he and his Damage Control Party sweated and heaved and generally manhandled the weighty shoring timbers from one end of the ship to the other. As the Chief Stoker said, 'Yew'd uv thought some fucker 'ould 'ave designed a stowage near the poxy bulkhead wot's likely to bleedin' cave in!'

Caucasian spent a week working up in this way, until the Captain was almost satisfied with the efficiency of every department of his ship. After a week of listening for the pipes and the action klaxon the ship's company were thoroughly relieved when it was all over and they could relax again. Even the 'dhobi-ing' sessions had been held in abeyance during the previous week of madness; this ritualistic washing of clothes and bodies having been prudently dropped after the action klaxon had sent half the ship's company to action stations in the nude.

Scotland's northern extremities, with their outcrop of barren rocky islands which sheltered the Home Fleet, could never profess to be beautiful or inviting, not even on a glorious day in the early summer of 1940; but this God-forsaken place of the north did possess a certain rugged grandeur and, as *Caucasian* neared the entrance to the anchorage, it presented a welcome sight indeed to her company, but only because it meant the end of a week of necessary lunacy. Scapa Flow had nothing to offer Jack.

The boom defence vessels operating at the entrance drew aside the anti-submarine nets, and the ship knifed proudly through the lines of bobbing marker buoys. Sleek and trim, with her cobwebs swept to the four winds, wearing her brand-new dress of best black and white arctic camouflage, with her company fallen in at 'stations for entering harbour', she made a handsome picture indeed, and proudly preened herself for the benefit of thousands of eyes with nothing better to do.

Wearing his best suit and his going-ashore cap the Captain stalked the upper bridge, his eyes everywhere as he watched for the slightest sign of slackness or unseaman-like conduct. His eyes missed nothing as they roved from fo'c's'le to quarterdeck and back again; he noted the cleanliness of the paintwork, the trim correctness of the boat stowage, the tightness of the standing rigging and the order of the hoist on the halyards, the trimly belayed ropes, and the hundred and one other points which bear witness to a ship's tightness. He scanned the water ahead of his ship to port, to starboard and astern; he noted the wind velocity and direction, watched the signal halyards of the flagship, anticipating the signal or the wink of an Aldis lamp which would bring a reproof because from the scurryings he saw on the flagship's flag deck through his telescope, he knew that the Commander-in-Chief was on deck, also with telescope trained.

As she steamed down through the lines of moored warships she was watched with keen professional interest by men who ranged from ordinary seamen to the C.-in-C. himself; men who had spent a lifetime in ships of the Fleet and knew precisely just how a ship should be handled, and anticipate nicely her every move. At that moment they were the most critical audience in the world; a false move and the Aldis lamp on the flagship would wink out a scathing enquiry and, if the gaffe was serious enough, a peremptory demand for the luckless Captain to wait upon the Rear Admiral (Destroyers) 'at your convenience' which meant immediately, or preferably yesterday morning before breakfast.

Caucasian made the customary courtesies. First a signal to the C.-in-C. reporting her arrival, and then to the Rear Admiral (D) and the Captain (D) for the same reason. Formal protocol dispensed with, it was time to relax a little and, after the new arrival had secured to her buoy, Aldis lamps from a dozen ships winked out a welcome.

With his ship safely moored Commander Philip St John Norton DSO, DSC, RN, feeling pleased with life and in a mood for sociability, addressed himself to his Chief Yeoman of Signals in time-honoured manner:

'Yeoman,' he snapped 'make a signal!'

'Aye, aye, Sir!' snapped back Chief Yeoman Harding.

The ever alert and watery-eyed 'Tosh' Harding – if he had another name nobody ever knew it – wiping a nose which never ceased to run, jumped to his lamp and with the alacrity of an ultra-efficient private secretary produced, seemingly out of thin air, a signal pad and, from behind his ear, conjured the inevitable stub of a pencil.

'To Captain (D) I4,' intoned the Captain 'and repeated all ships (D) I4. Signal begins, "Delighted to be home again. Many thanks your felicitations. RPC (request the pleasure of your company) 1830 this day," signal ends.'

Tosh was 'wanking' (working) the handle of his lamp before the Captain finished speaking. Captain (D) was lying a few cable lengths to port, and as soon as *Caucasian*'s Aldis ceased to blink back came the reply: 'WMP (with much pleasure). Will appreciate the fresh Plymouth (gin); ours contaminated with salt water'.

The Captain smiled wryly at this none too subtle allusion to his ship's recent sojourn in dock and, fixing the grinning Tosh with the official gimlet eye, snapped: 'Thank you, Yeoman... that'll be all.'

Tosh pulled a face at the retreating back of his Captain, sniffed one of his sniffs, and mumbled: 'Acid bastard!' When the back was out of earshot of course.

'Right yew showera brown 'atters (homosexuals)... clear the bridge!'

His staff leapt to obey, and in no time at all the bridge was all shipshape and the staff disappeared below decks. Tosh lit a Woodbine which he took from a battered old tin and, leaning on the flag locker, gazed pensively out upon the mighty concourse of warships gathered there, girt about by the barren, rock-bound shore of Orkney. There were ships of all sizes from the lowly little Flower Class corvettes to the mighty battle-wagons and aircraft carriers; in the arctic gales and off the coast of Norway he had weathered it out with most of them. Despite the illusion of peace he always got the feeling of being poised on the eve of great events in this lonely bastion of the northern ocean.

Tosh was a veteran of the First World War, eight months of the Second World War, and one sinking. 'Bleedin' Norway 'ad been no bloody picnic either.' *Caucasian* had steamed up Narvik Fjord into an inferno of fire and counterfire; a holocaust of screaming, crashing shells. He had been at his action station on the upper bridge, side by side with his Captain, right under the heavy guns of *Warspite* as she sent broadside after broadside whining and crashing into the enemy ships and shore installations. ' 'Nuff ta give any bastard the bleedin' screaming abdabs.' He sniffed, rubbed his watery eyes, and turned to go below. Not much doing today. Another bomb casualty would be returning to the flotilla tomorrow, and he'd be on the bridge to see her in. HMS *Mohawk* had copped hers under the Forth Bridge – of all places. The Yeoman of *Mohawk* was a chum of his, and he was dying to see the old bastard's face when he saw his (Tosh's) DSM, plus a Mention in the Canteen Chit-Book (Mention in Despatches); that was a couple of decorations due for a thorough wetting at about eleven o'clock-ish on the morrow.

Below decks all was bustle and activity as the hands changed into working dress and dinner was prepared. Everyone seemed to be doing everything at once and getting in each other's way.

The time being a trifle before eleven o'clock, in the Seamen's Mess 'Stripey' – John Augustus – Ackers was getting ready the rum 'fanny' (pan) and tot measures before drawing the 'bubbly' (rum). In time-honoured fashion, on the end of the messdeck table was placed a damp cloth to prevent the glasses from slipping. A shallow tray, by courtesy of Messrs Ind Coope and Allsopp, and by nature of being a hard-won trophy of the chase – it having been stolen from some pub or other – was placed over the cloth to catch the precious fluid should it by some deadly mischance be spilled. Perish the thought! Also arranged, in due form and according to ancient tradition, was an odd assortment of tot 'glasses', ranging from LMS railway teacups, minus handles, to Wardroom wineglasses which had been nicked 'down aft,' and an elegantly stemmed wineglass, decorated with a richly adorned Spanish flamenco dancer on the outside, whilst on the inside she was naked and striking an exceedingly inelegant pose. This last was 'Stripey's' glass; a chalice, the eucharistic wine cup, as sacred as any altar piece; which, indeed, it was – a Bacchanalian altar piece. Each man in the mess had his own glass, cup, or mug, and woe betide the man who dared to use the wrong one; unless, of course, invited so to do by its rightful owner.

'Stripey' Ackers disappeared in the direction of the rum 'tub' to draw the daily issue of 'Nelson's Blood' – a privilege exclusively his. In most ships this privilege is normally accorded to each member of the mess over twenty years of age, on a strict rota system. But not here in *Caucasian*, indeed not; here the prerogative was strictly 'Stripey's', a concession for which he had wheedled, fought, and intrigued for months. He now guarded jealously his status as permanent 'bubbly bosun', and let no man gainsay him.

'Can't fer the life o' me un'erstan' it,' 'Scouse' Orrigan was saying to his 'oppo', and to anyone else prepared to listen. 'They pipes the bleedin' 'ands ta clean inta the rig o' the bleedin' day fer enterin' 'arbour, so yew gets inta a decent suit o' blues an' yew falls in fer enterin' 'arbour, an' shag me if yew don't spend the next 'alf hour gallopin' round the poxy upper deck wiv dirty great greasy wires, then yew comes back down below ta change inta Number 8s (working dress) to do work wot's a bloody sight cleaner than enterin' 'arbour!'

'Scouse' was the 'buoy jumper'; he should know, and heads nodded in agreement. They had heard it all before.

'An' all because,' continued 'Scouse', 'some fat ol' bastard uv a admiral' (this in his best toffy-nosed Wardroom accent) 'laikes tay see his jollay old saylars lookin' all naice an' tiddly (smart) when they entahs harba'... fair gives me the shits it do!'

The arrival of 'Stripey' and the rum fanny brought everyone crowding around the messdeck table, and 'Stripey' opened the daily ritual with the self-evident pronouncement 'Bubbly's up!' The heady smell of rum pervaded the mess, the hands foregathered at the fanny, and the dispensation began:

'Wilt thou partake of a soupçon of wine?' asked one wit of his friend.

'Delighted me deah boy,' and a 'sipper' was drunk with solemn dignity and true appreciation.

'Jan boy, yew owes me a 'gulper' fer findin' yer pen yesterday,' and a gulp was consumed as a token of thanks.

'*Nunc est bibendum*,' murmured another, without the slightest idea of what it meant; it was just an expression which he had picked up somewhere or other; he knew that it had something to do with booze; it was his favourite tot-time expression, and he rolled the precious fluid around his palate like a *Chevalier du Tastevin* at a vintage tasting.

'Stripey' Ackers was holding forth, as he did at the same time every day of his life; with his tot held up to the light of the porthole he squinted at it short-sightedly, then turned to the assembled company and uttered his daily benediction: 'Gen'lemen... I gives yew a toast.'

He paused impressively; he always did. ' 'ere's to wimmin, cards and dice, pox an' syphilis, crabs an' lice. God bless the ladies.' The usual dutiful titter was raised, and 'Stripey' downed his tot in one.

'Mick the Dick' O'Malley – so called because he was the proud owner of the biggest private part in the Royal Navy – from the Emerald Isle was repaying a debt: 'Sippers you may have my friend, an' God bless yer 'onour's grace!'

'Stripey,' meanwhile, was collecting his dues from his messmates, and from them to all the other messes in the ship where members were indebted to ol' 'Stripes' for services rendered. For a 'sipper' he would stitch badge or button on a jacket, jumper, or overcoat, or put the regulation seven box creases in a sailor's bell-bottom trousers in semi-permanence – a knack which he possessed, and a trade secret. For 'gulpers' he would stitch on a whole set of badges or buttons, mend tears, and insert patches that really were invisible, or steal an extra bar of soap from the Cleaning Gear Store. The promise of a full tot could raise him to the very acme of industrious endeavour and cunning in his efforts to fulfil the wishes of the promiser, and for a permanent option on a tot he would sell his soul to the devil or his grandmother 'up the creek'. But, for all his cunning and his addiction to the bottle, he never did a poor job. 'Leave it to ol' 'Stripey' ' was his watchword, and leave it one could, in absolute confidence; and, despite the amount of rum he drank, he never seemed to get drunk or suffer ill effects.

The grog disposed of, dinner eaten, a smoke, a natter, and back to work for the afternoon, doing the many jobs necessary to maintain the ship at full fighting efficiency. Guns to clean, grease, and test, ready for action, torpedoes to run out and overhaul, depth charges and magazines to check, decks to scrub and paintwork to touch up. *Caucasian* had to be ready for sea. With sailing orders likely to come at any moment the First Lieutenant drove everyone hard. The nattering and the cussing which accompanied the process was music to his ears; the boys, after the docking period, were really back on song. Give 'em something to moan about, contended 'Jimmy' (First Lieutenant), and the result was a happy ship. It was when they were not moaning, blaspheming, and generally bewailing the lot of the luckless sailor that trouble could be expected. It would mean that they were suffering from the malignancy of boredom, and from boredom was mischief bred.

From two in the afternoon to six o'clock in the evening canteen leave was granted to one watch, with two beer tickets issued to each man who mustered to go ashore. Two pints of beer was no good to any man possessing a predilection for the stuff; and, consequently, the racketeers swung into action immediately the pipe was made. A thriving trade in beer tickets sprang up. The result of such transactions resulted in comparatively few men drinking a great number of pints in a comparatively short time, and returning in the liberty boats to their respective ships in carnival mood, singing, shouting, and cheering like schoolboys at a bun fight.

Fights there were but, in the main, it was singing beer the NAAFI dispensed in the Fleet Canteen at Flotta in Scapa Flow.

Interdivisional rivalries played their part, as they always do in any gathering together of the ships of the fleet. Whether it is in the matter of efficiency, cleanliness of ship, the Fleet Regatta, or just plain cussedness, rivalry runs riot. Such rivalry is healthy, and is nurtured dearly by officers and men alike. After 'Time' had been called, and the canteen was cleared by a much harassed Shore Patrol, the liberty boats in their hundreds chugged around the Fleet delivering whole boatloads of high-spirited, beer-besotted matelots back to their respective ships. The rivalries, always simmering in the pot of divisionalism (naval divisions), reached their peak and erupted into singing, shouting, cheering, chanting and just plain 'fer the 'ell uv it'. Everyone knew which ship was manned by which Division; Devonport, Portsmouth, or Chatham. HMS *Renown* was Devonport manned; so, as the liberty boats drew level with the battle cruiser's gangway, the sailors burst forth with the 'oggy song'.

' 'Alf a pound uv flour an' lard
Makes a luvly clacker (pastry).
Jest enuff fer yew an' me,
Poor bugger Jacker (West Country man).'

And finished off on a note of high nostalgia:

' 'O 'ow 'appy us'll be
When us gets back to the West Countryeeeee,
Where the oggies (Cornish pasties) grow on trees,
Poor bugger Jacker – the sod!'

Followed by cheers which could be heard from one end of the Flow to the other. 'Oggy, oggy, oggy! – go ta sea yew showera loafing sods – get some bleedin' sea time in!'

Portsmouth, to score a vocal ascendancy, started to chant, letter by letter, 'P-O-R-T-S-M-O-U-T-H – Portsmouth!' and the ' 'Ampshire 'ogs' was sung to the tune of *The Farmer's Boy*. More wild cheering, and then cries of 'Chatty, chatty (scruffy), Chatham!... yew showera crabby bastards!' with a heartfelt rendition of *The Old Kent Road* (Naval version).

At the head of gangways Officers of the Day fumed impotently, and in vain shouted for 'Silence in the boats!' Heads appeared from portholes, and the hands lined the guardrails to lend vocal support to the proceedings. Below decks officers frowned disapprovingly into pink gins. Captains, in the grand isolation of their cabins, winced and told their stewards to close the portholes. Admirals, in the exalted exclusiveness of their 'cuddies' (Admiral's quarters) smiled indulgently; nothing much wrong with chaps who could create that much noise. Morale in the Fleet was at its singing, shouting, abusive best.

Such was the nation's first line of defence in the summer of 1940; here in the morale of the men of the Fleet was the war to be won or lost. As Taff Davies, Able Seaman, remarked to Johnny Thomas, 'If we can't beat the bastards at sea we'll sing the fuckers to deaf (death)!'

The last load of libertymen were delivered to their ships, boats went to their booms, or were hoisted into davits, the merrymakers disappeared below decks and, as the evening approached, potent, brooding normality returned to the Flow. For the men of the Home Fleet action was always just around the corner.

In *Caucasian*, as she swung peacefully at her buoy, all was snug and the messdecks settled into the evening routine. 'Dhobi-ing' (clothes washing) sessions were well under way in the bathrooms, letters were written to loved ones, the cards appeared and noses were buried in books. Some argued, whilst others just sat around and talked. Every possible topic was good for an airing. Politics, the cinema, the war, reminiscences of home and the missus and kids, the girlfriend; and, as was ever thus, Sex, with a capital S, was mulled over. Sex was a topic of which the messdecks never tired.

'We gets fanny fer breakfast, dinner, tea an' bleedin' supper, an' all the times in between... an' be Jaysus, that's me favourite subject!'

One of *Caucasian*'s ship's company wrote poetry, and could be prevailed upon, occasionally, to read his verse to certain of the more appreciative members of the mess. Yet another was building a model of the ship with matchsticks.

Further activity was stilled by the trilling of the bos'un's call; the Coxswain entered the messdecks preceded by the bos'un's mate with his 'built-in budgerigar,' and followed by the Officer of the Day who was doing his evening rounds (inspection).

' 'Tenshun fer rounds!' snarled the Coxswain.

Everyone snapped to attention; even those already in their hammocks lay down at attention. The OOD walked through the mess, his eyes probing everywhere, ferreting out the dirty corners and generally assuring himself that all was as it should be – Shipshape and Bristol fashion. The Coxswain's barked order to 'carry on' indicated that all was well in the Seamen's Mess.

'Carry on,' mimicked one of the wits; 'I'd like ta carry on wiv that bastard!' – *sotto voce*, of course.

'Don't fancy 'im meself,' replied another. 'A bit bleedin' 'airy round the ass... give me a nice little party uv about sixteen wot ain't never 'ad it yet!'

'Silence in the mess!' snarled the Coxswain, glowering back over his shoulder, ' 'relse yew'll 'ave it, Able Seaman Lee... on the quarterdeck wiv yer 'at at the dip!' (As a preliminary to legal proceedings a sailor always removes his hat.)

After the OOD and his retinue had passed, the remaining hammocks were slung and the hands made ready for the night. Johnny Thomas, peering over the top of his hammock enquired of his friend the Professor: 'How's about a shower before turning in?'

The two friends collected toilet gear and wended their way aft to the bathroom. The sounds of the nightly ablutions reached their ears before the door of the bathroom was reached, and they entered what can only be described as a bacchanal of hot water and soap suds. Steam billowed everywhere, the deck was awash, and naked bodies flitted through this aquatic phantasmagoria like phantoms in a London fog. Others bent diligently over dhobi-ing buckets which bore strange shipboard legends painted on their sides: 'Stripey's tub – hands off,' 'Captain of the Heads (lavatory cleaner) – not to be removed from the shithouse,' 'Captain, personal – if found return to Dodger Long' or 'No 1 Boiler Room – not to be used for oil fuel, or else!'

Everyone in the bathroom was either singing, whistling – a practice frowned upon in the Navy because it might have been confused with the pipes – or shouting a conversation above the din. Everywhere hung dripping clothes. In the showers the close harmony group, led by 'Jan' Abbott – 'the Bishop' – gave forth with the Toreador's Song from Bizet's *Carmen*. The vocal opposition, under the direction of Maestro Young, Leading Stoker of this parish, offered their rendition of 'Drake is in 'is 'ammick a fowsand leagues away,' whilst in the far corner 'Newfy' – because he hailed from Newfoundland – Hesketh howled his own inimitable version of the aria from *Madam Butterfly*. The remainder hummed, sang, shouted, fought with wet towels, and threw buckets of water over each other. And all this in a space no bigger than a suburban bedroom.

The proximity of 'Pipe Down' brought the proceedings to a reluctant close. Reluctant because there was something friendly and intimate about a dhobi-ing session. It did a man a power of good to fill his lungs and raise his voice in song, and to dhobi his body, his personal effects, and his soul.

The Duty Petty Officer poked a disapproving head around the bathroom door, and bawled: 'Come away yew showera crabby bastards... wrappitup... Pipe Down in five minutes!'

'Get knotted!' said 'Pappy' Pringle to the closed door, having made sure first that the Duty PO was well on his way for'ard. 'Pappy,' a big, raw-boned, hard-drinking, hard-swearing product of Britain's oldest colony, Newfoundland, preened his massive frame in front of the mirror.

'Gee honey,' said he to a purely illusory female whom only he could see reflected there, 'jist yew wait 'till liddle ol' 'Pappy' gits back 'ome!' and he hugged her imaginary body to his great hairy chest, and made amorous noises suggestive of a mating grizzly bear; then, pausing for a moment, the self-appointed one man admiration committee frowned at itself in the mirror and fingered the scar on its right cheek; a scar deeply incised by the razor of one of a gang of Glasgow hooligans, which he would carry to the end of his days. The hoodlums had reason to regret their encounter with 'Pappy'; he had gone berserk, and left St Enoch's Square littered with their injured; the rest hotfooting it to other parts of the city. By all accounts 'Pappy,' streaming blood, had exacted a terrible vengeance with fists, boots and a bicycle chain taken from one of his assailants.

'C'mon Prof'; his slap on the back nearly sent that worthy reeling, naked, through the bathroom door. 'Away ta yer aeriel sofa... yew 'eard wot the man said!' The Professor made a feint and squared up to the great barrel chest. 'Away wid ya,' boomed 'Pappy' with a playful swipe, 'Afore I beats yer bleedin' 'ead in!' They were the best of friends and were given to talking by the hour.

'I guess I ain't 'ad no edicayshun, Prof,' he had said early in their acquaintanceship, 'but I guess I ain't too goddamned old to larn,' and, whenever he could get a word in, he regaled his learned messmate with tales of his pre-war life in the fishing boats which worked Newfoundland's Grand Banks.

As the bathroom leeches tumbled back down the messdeck ladder the pre-Pipe Down horseplay was suddenly and dramatically stilled by the unexpected trilling of the Bos'un's Call. There was an expectant silence as the intercom began to crackle.

'This is the Captain speaking; I shall not keep you long. It appears that our holiday is over. Within the last fifteen minutes I have received orders from the Commander-in-Chief; we get under way at midnight.' The ensuing groan must have been audible to the Captain in his cabin. 'As yet I am not at liberty to tell you where we are going; to be honest I do not know myself, but in keeping with my policy to keep you all completely in the picture, I shall let you know as soon as I am permitted so to do, but that will not be before we clear harbour and get well out to sea. Tomorrow we shall all be in full possession of the facts, but this I am able to tell you: we are on to something special.' More groans; the Tribals were always on to something special. 'So let's get down to bringing the ship to peak fighting efficiency, just in case in the weeks and months that lie ahead we have to fight something, somewhere. Before closing may I take this opportunity of thanking you all for the splendid work you have put in since the ship came out of dock; she is in tip top form, let's keep her that way, and we shall prove more than a match for anything which comes along. In less than two hours we shall be under way. May God go with us. That is all. Goodnight, gentlemen.'

'Where's that buzz-spreadin' bastard uv a Captain's Steward?' demanded Jackie Fisher, the Leading Torpedoman. 'I bet 'e knows, the sod... prob'ly told the ol' man anyway!'

But it was a subdued messdeck that took to its hammocks that night; and the Captain's Steward, 'Dodger' Long, would not have been able to enlighten them anyway; even his buzz-spreading proclivities would not stretch that far. Besides he was in his hammock already, right down aft in his little mess under the Wardroom, and it took more than unexpected orders for sea to disturb the good 'Dodger's' equilibrium. Wearing a pair of silk pyjamas, and reading a luridly jacketed piece of Americana entitled *Dead Blondes Don't Talk* he 'cocked a deaf un' because at that precise moment when the pipe was made he was roaring down Broadway in the city of New York in a getaway car hotly pursued by the District Attorney and the Homicide Squad.

The Stewards, by virtue of the hours they worked and the nature of their duties, were a privileged community; they lived in a mess of their own where 'Dodger' reigned supreme. Generally 'Dodger' and his minions went their own way, not too much disturbed by things nautical; and 'Dodger' was to some extent a law unto himself. The only time the Duty Petty Officer entered 'Dodger's' domain was by invitation and to partake of a little light refreshment from the Captain's gin bottle.

It was with the merest flicker of awareness, and another sip of a large 'pink un,' that he realized that the screws had started to turn beneath him. The ship was under way; so what? Plenty of time to give thought to that matter tomorrow morning; meanwhile, back to New York and the blonde.

'Dodger' was the proud possessor of two Good Conduct Badges (at least eight years of 'undetected crime') and a Leading Rate and, come hell's fire or enemy shot, he was never ruffled; always the same imperturbable urbanity, whether down in the bowels of the ship at Action Stations – he was in charge of the after magazine – or tippling the Captain's gin; he never changed. In the piping days of peace he had served in the Royal Yacht, his accents were those of the perfect gentleman's gentleman – his father was a butler in one of England's stately homes – his manners impeccable, and from his gold cuff links to his silk socks he was a model of how the well-dressed Steward should be dressed. His failings, if failings indeed they were, were a marked liking for the Captain's – or anyone else's – gin, an ardent desire to propagate the human species, and a propensity for spreading 'buzzes'. A confirmed ladies' man, he spent his life one jump ahead of irate husbands and paternity orders.

Only slightly conscious of the screws pounding away beneath him, 'Dodger' read on; he had learnt to live with the noise of the ship's propulsion years ago. On deck all was darkness, the deep inky darkness of a clouded summer's night. The sky was heavily overcast, the air oppressive, and away in the distance an occasional flash of lightning told of an electric storm somewhere out on the broad expanse of the North Atlantic. The sea was heavy and placid and the ship dipped with an easy motion into the long offshore swell. An ideal night for the ships of war to slip quietly to sea. Darkness was their ally because it protected them from prying eyes, enemy eyes that kept a constant watch on the ships of the Fleet from the shores of Orkney. It also hid them from the U-Boats which lurked off the entrance to the anchorage on the edge of the minefields through which *Caucasian* and her consorts now threaded their cautious way.

Caucasian rose and dipped with a long easy motion, now rolling slightly to port, now to starboard, now pitching gently as she gathered speed. On her bridge the Captain and his officers, and the lookouts and bridge watchkeepers, breathed deep the salt-laden air, and strained their eyes into a sightless night heavy with the threat of rain. In the near distance could faintly be seen the silver froth of the wake of a ship, but of the ship nothing. The Captain's hands, groping instinctively in the darkness, found the familiar shape of the compass binnacle and he could see, faintly glowing, the illuminated compass card jerking slightly as the Quartermaster at the wheel on the deck below responded to course and helm. On the side bridge the shadowy figures of the lookouts moved and, somewhere behind him, he could hear the Chief Yeoman sniffing. Below the compass platform and a little forward the navigating officer was mumbling to himself as he worked out course and speed on the charts spread on the table of his caboose under a dim light.

The Captain breathed deep and appreciatively, filling his lungs with the fresh unpolluted air of the northern ocean, and feeling the cool caress of the breeze on his face. Through the soles of his feet he could feel the faint rhythmic throb of the engines. In the night he could hear his ship talking to him, and with all his heart he replied. He felt at one with his environment; he was back where he belonged. He was home again; and he thought of his other home, the place where his wife and children lived. He thought too of the men asleep below decks. He gave thought as well to the enemy out there ahead of his ship; also he thought of tomorrow, and all the other tomorrows and what the future held in store for him and his ship. What was that thing he had learned at school – W.E. Henley, wasn't it?

'It matters not how strait the gate,
How charged with punishments the scroll,
I am the master of my fate:
I am the captain of my soul.'

He strained his eyes into the night, watching for the slightest sign of the unusual – if U-Boats and surface raiders could be termed unusual in these waters – and for anything that could, at a moment's notice, set the alarm klaxons blaring and the ship's company scrambling madly to action stations.

Chapter 4

Malta Convoy

'Nothing has been neglected on my part to get supplies to Malta, and by the greatest exertions, for this country is in absolute want.... The Kingdom of Naples is full of corn.'

Rear Admiral Lord Nelson to Commodore Sir Thomas Troubridge Bt.
8 January, 1800.

As *Caucasian* and her sister destroyers steamed steadily to the south the days grew warmer and the sea more placid, and her ship's company were light of heart and went about their affairs in high good humour. Sunbathing was much in vogue, and bodies tanned under the increasing heat of the sun and warm ocean breezes. Stripped to the waist matelots sprawled everywhere. It was forbidden to get down to the buff and, because the action klaxon could sound off at any moment, anti-flash gear was kept handy by Order of the Day. Action Stations were no place for naked men.

'Sludge' Coles was taking his customary afternoon siesta, stretched out in the lee of the port after-gun-sponson, when an enterprising shipmate cut a stencil in stiff brown paper and applied it to the sleeping 'Sludge's' back. The hot afternoon sun did the rest. The result? Hilarity from his messmates every time he took his shirt off. Howls of laughter from his mates, and howls of indignation from 'Sludge' when he discovered the reason why. There in letters six inches high was the legend 'I'm a cunt.' Next day 'Sludge' wreaked a just and terrible vengeance with a hosepipe. Unfortunately he failed to apply the vengeful pipe with due discretion and flushed out sleepers and afternoon nappers indiscriminately. Half the ship's company, including some very senior members thereof, were half-drowned, and 'Sludge' was last seen that day heading for the bowels of the ship hotly pursued by an irate Chief Stoker with murder in his heart and a spanner in his hand.

After the dirt and grime of Liverpool's dockland, and the wintry northern summers, the journey to the south and the sun was welcomed; even the Captain took off his shirt and lounged, ever so slightly, in his high chair on the bridge. Bathing was out of the question, so hosepipes were deployed and aquatic battles raged most afternoons when there was a 'make and mend clothes' (that is, afternoon off for that purpose).

The relaxation acted like a tonic, and the further south they steamed the less likelihood there was of U-Boats. These predators had yet to bring into use the bases on the western coast of France which were to increase so effectively their operational range a few months later. In *Caucasian* the skylarking received official blessing from a wise – and partially blind – Captain, but lookouts were maintained; there was no relaxation of alertness.

Caucasian and the rest of the flotilla, of which she was now leader, having left the Senior Officer in *Cossack* at Scapa Flow, were escorting a convoy composed mainly of fast troopships part of the way to Cape Town and East Africa, ultimately to unload at Port Tewfik at the Red Sea end of the Suez Canal. They were laden with reinforcements for General Wavell's army in the Western Desert. Italy had recently declared war on the Allies and could be expected in the desert at any moment. Hence the presence of the powerful Tribals in the escort; this was a very important convoy, and this was a surface raider area. Somewhere in the region 25 degrees west, 20 degrees north the escort would hand over to the Freetown (British West Africa) escort group and steam back to Gibraltar. The question was, where from Gib? To date the Captain had acquainted the ship's company only with that part of the operation which concerned the convoy escort; they would know the rest when the ship left the Rock.

On *Caucasian's* port after-lookout position the Professor stumped backwards and forwards waiting for his relief at 0800; behind him the gun turret was bathed in the glowing light of dawn; before him stretched to a vast horizon the wide heaving bosom of the Atlantic, dotted here and there with the growing outline of ships in convoy. Another dawn, another day. All was peaceful and still when, suddenly, right where the Professor looked, the early light was rent by a brilliant sheet of flame which licked and flickered skyward and, after what seemed an age, there came to the horrified watchers, the dull roar of an explosion.

For a brief moment the Professor gazed stupefied at the stricken ship; it was the first time he had witnessed the tragedy of war at sea, and for a while he failed to grasp the significance of what he saw. From that distance it was hard to discern who or what she was, and the licking flames and billowing smoke made it even harder to recognize her. Suddenly, shattering the peace of below decks, the action klaxon blared out its insistent message, and the ship's company scrambled madly to action stations.

Within minutes the ship was manned and ready for action as soon as the enemy was detected. Was it submarine or surface raider? Intent on finding out *Caucasian* increased speed to thirty knots, signalled all ships to take the prearranged evasive action and, with bunting flying and Aldis flashing, she raced towards the stricken ship. Perhaps it was a U-Boat, or could it be a surface raider? If the latter it could only mean a pocket battleship; the range was too great for anything smaller. Perhaps *Bismarck* was out and in the area; or could it be *Scharnhorst*?

Caucasian's speed went up to thirty-five knots and, pulsating and leaping, she surged forward with threshing wake and bow wave creaming. Whatever lay out there, it was all down to her. God only knew where the nearest cruisers were. Primed and ready she swung to where the blazing troopship – for such it transpired she was – lay stark and terrible upon the sea. But not for *Caucasian* the errand of mercy; she left such things to lesser ships – the corvettes and sloops of the escort. She headed to where *Echo* had just dropped a pattern of depth charges and, as she swept past the blazing troopship, her company gazed hard-eyed and silent upon the dreadful scene.

The once proud passenger liner was a raging inferno; she must have been hit in the boiler room; her fractured fuel lines were pumping thousands of gallons of oil into the ocean. Flames licked her superstructure and mounted like a gigantic funeral pyre into the cloudless sky. Blazing men could be seen running screaming about her decks and plunging into the burning sea.

Caucasian's dash to the suspect area proved fruitless; her anti-submarine equipment and a dozen patterns of depth charges failed to rouse even the slightest suspicion of a U-Boat; yet U-Boat it must have been; the horizon was devoid of the slightest sign of any other ship. The hunt continued well into the morning. Nothing. She returned to the scene of the blazing ship. Rescue ships nudged as close as they dared, pushing aside what looked like hunks of charred timber or blackened carcasses; these were the bodies of men. Those who still lived screamed and thrashed the water in agony. Here and there men swam silently, seemingly unhurried, heads, shoulders and arms black and viscous with oil. These were the lucky ones. These were the survivors. Paint blistered on the sides of the rescue ships, and rescue was a long and ghastly business; only the obviously living were picked up; the dead, the oh, so obviously dead, were left to find graves where they could; the sea, in cold indifference, would perform their funeral rites.

Just before noon the troopship was no more. With a fearful hissing of white-hot metal she slipped ungraciously to her last resting place; the only reminder that a once proud ship had passed over these waters was a huge patch of oil-fouled sea, and a dwindling area of debris and charred bodies.

By this time the convoy was hull down on the horizon to the south; before regaining station *Caucasian* circled the debris with dipped ensign in salute to the memory of dead men and a fine ship.

After this hideous experience the atmosphere in the Escort Leader changed; spirits became subdued. Here again was the stark reality of war.

The Professor was haunted by the memory of the troopship's end, and of the fate of the troops and seamen aboard her. Nearly fifteen hundred men had died a horrible death, and God knows how many more died aboard the rescue ships. His whole being revolted against the horror of that dawn, and against the lack of humanity in man. In the days that followed he relived the scene over and over again; he saw the cautiously scanning periscope of the U-boat, saw the rangefinders converging and the concentration on the face of her Captain as he pressed the button which sent the torpedoes unerringly upon their track to the target, and he saw and heard again the flash and roar of the explosion. He heard also the shouts of jubilation of her crew as she turned away and dived deep to avoid her pursuers. The thought that nagged at the Professor most was knowing that, in the same position, he would have done exactly the same.

Next morning, after the sinking of the troopship, an uneventful dawn greeted night-strained eyes and, saying 'Goodbye, good luck, and God speed' to the southbound convoy, *Caucasian* and her consorts turned north about for Gibraltar. With the southbound convoy went *Encounter* which, fighting side by side with the legendary *Exeter* of Battle of the River Plate fame, was to fight the Battle of the Java Sea when, ringed about by the guns of the Japanese fleet, she fought to a standstill, and her company – those that is who survived – found years of bestiality and degradation at the hands of their Japanese captors.

When *Caucasian* slipped into Gibraltar harbour, Dunkirk had passed into history, Italy had declared war, and the clouds of war piled high on the Mediterranean horizons; hence the presence of *Caucasian* and her flotilla here in the shadow of the Rock. She and her consorts, in anticipation of further moves on the part of the Axis powers, were bound for Alexandria. '*Drang Nach Osten*' had not been buried in the cemeteries of Flanders. With the change of regime in Germany, Middle Eastern oil had in no way lost its attraction. Under Adolf Hitler the opposite was the case, the desire to go east was stronger. It was an economic and strategic necessity, essential to the maintenance of the Nazi war machine. Without oil the Panzer Divisions and the *Luftwaffe* would become heaps of useless scrap; with it their potential to prosecute war was unlimited; the *Wehrmacht* might stand guard at Vladivostok, or watch the tides eddy about the Cape of Good Hope.

Meanwhile at the feet of the matelots lay Gibraltar. For many it was their first foreign port of call; it might be their last; 'so slacken yer garters, Main Street, 'ere we come!' To men accustomed to northern climes, and the cold winds of the North Atlantic, the heat on the Rock was stifling. The sun beat down with a merciless intensity from a cloudless sky and was deflected in shimmering waves from the white stone buildings and denuded rock faces. The town and beaches teemed with sailors from the ships which sought haven beneath the towering fortress or rode at anchor in Algeciras Bay. Jack was everywhere; stretched out on the beaches, in the bars – especially the bars – in the cafés, souvenir shops, sleeping it off under the trees and in sheltered spots in the parks and public places, and filling the Forces' canteens until the bulkheads bulged.

As yet Gibraltar knew no war. The effects of Italy's entry into the war had yet to be felt; consequently Main Street boomed like a western cattle town, and it even boasted batwing doors to its saloons. The doors, it was alleged, were designed to facilitate Jack's exit to the street when he was thrown out on his ear. A not uncommon occurrence. The bars provided Spanish dancers, and the air of the place reverberated to the music of guitars, the tap-tap-tap of high-heeled shoes, the clacking of castanets, and the olés and bravos of drunken matelots. There was no bullring in Gibraltar, but for all the enthusiasm shouted to 'torro, torro' there might well have been. Liquor, from English beer to the heady Malaga wines and the 'geek' of the 'boiled oil shops' flowed in a stream which only ceased to flow when the curfew was imposed at half an hour before sunset. For little more than the price of a packet of cigarettes Jack could get paralytically drunk – and did – provided he possessed no scruples about the brand and origin of the booze he drank. And Jack had few scruples on that score – booze was booze the world over.

In the cabarets – The Universal, The Trocadero, The Café Suisse (the ol' Squeeze-Box) – the hostesses catered for the sailor's every need except one, and that was taboo: 'You can screw over the border, Jack, but not 'ere; ther' ain't no broffels in Gib.' The ladies drank nothing but coloured water at best booze prices, and for every glass they drank they made sure that Jack drank, and paid for, two. The ladies were on commission. The bands blared, and the matelots sang, wolf-whistled, fought, danced and lay in the gutters. Bottles and glasses were smashed, tables overturned, women screamed and scratched when hands dived up their skirts and inert bodies crashed through batwing doors. The dancers were encouraged to fantastic feats of agility by the howls of approving – or disapproving – sailors, the orchestras performed yeoman service against formidable odds and, as the evening wore on, verbal battles royal raged between orchestras and audiences. Wild shouting, cheering, fiddle-scraping, drum-beating battles that never would reach a conclusion until the shutters went down. It was not unknown for such affairs to end up with the drummer's head being fitted into his own drum, orchestra and hostesses scattering out through the side door, and Jack spewing out in a struggling, fighting, cursing and laughing body of high spirits onto the street, assisted by the Naval Provost Marshall and his men.

By sunset Gibraltar was a ghost town with not a sailor to be seen, and behind heavily shuttered doors and windows mine hosts of Main Street counted the day's takings, assessed the day's damage, adjusted tomorrow's prices accordingly, and took themselves off to bed. Tomorrow would see a repeat performance. Whatever the philosophy of mine hosts of Main Street – perhaps it was an indulgent patriotism – Jack never paid a penny damages, and always found a welcome next time ashore.

Apart from swimming in the afternoon and high life on Main Street in the evening Gibraltar offered little else by way of diversion, except sport, of the outdoor, athletic variety. Soccer, on a pitch concrete hard, and in the blazing heat of day, drew an immense and lively crowd; a very vociferous crowd which, at times, reached the proportions of an FA Cup Final. The interest aroused was greatly enhanced by players of international repute serving in the Fleet throughout the war. Indeed one particular battleship fielded a full international side.

The Professor and Johnny Thomas found daily exercise and diversion by walking up the southern end of the Rock to see the apes, and descending via Moorish Castle at the northwest corner. They welcomed the opportunity to get away from the ship for a few hours of walking and talking with the mountains of Andalusia and the Sierra Nevada away to the north, and the coast of Tangier to the south; behind them was the broad, misty vastness of the Atlantic, and before them the shimmering, ominously smiling blue of the Mediterranean. This was thinking country, and what better man to think with than the Professor? Walking, talking and idly flickering over the pages of history, he was an admirable guide to these historic heights, and Johnny Thomas listened like a pupil to the erudition of his friend.

Historically, he said, Gibraltar had played a major role in the development of mankind. He ranged the field of its history from the volcanic eruption which had thrown up this citadel, and traced its story through the Dynastic days of Ancient Egypt, through the Phoenician, Greek, Roman, Moorish, and British eras to the present day.

As Johnny Thomas listened he reflected on the words of his friend. He had never thought about such things in the past, and from the train of thought started by his messmate, he realized that the world had been civilized largely by ordinary chaps like himself. The religion, the arts, the sciences, the culture, the very essence of Britain had been spread abroad and borne in British ships, husbanded by British sailors. The Navy assumed a new meaning; it was like being part of a great crusade. He learned a new, different pride in the uniform he wore, and in the flag under which he served. There was more to being a matelot than 'baggin' off' (wenching) in Devonport, or pissin' yer wages against the wall.

'Of course' the Professor was saying as they descended the hill from Moorish Castle for the last time of their stay in Gibraltar, 'it all comes down to education; education is the great equalizer; partly educate a man and he starts to fight for a greater share of the world's goods, and who's to blame him? It's the basic motive power of all progress. Finish his education – if such a thing is possible – and he realizes the folly of fighting. It's as simple as that.'

Don't sound very bloody simple to me, thought Johnny.

'Meanwhile,' the Professor smiled wryly, 'we have a war on our hands, a date with a skinful of ale, and we can't wait till the world gets educated, son. Hey ho! back to the fleshpots!'

Soon they were back on Main Street, and the fleshpots were doing very nicely, thank you. They joined a few shipmates and found the rest of *Caucasian*'s ship's company whooping it up in one of the bars, celebrating the last night in harbour and, within the hour, were as drunk as a pair of skunks. Drink and be merry, for tomorrow we sail.

Such was the philosophy of the men who, on the morrow, would force the narrows of the Italian lake. That night was the eve of sailing for so many of the ships in harbour. Spirits were higher, the songs louder and the fights more fierce.

The Professor collected a black eye, given him by a Stoker from the battle cruiser *Renown*, and all because he, the Professor desired to hold hands whilst singing Auld Lang Syne. The Stoker had misconstrued his motives and 'hung one on him'.

Eventually all the sailors, more by luck than sober judgement, found their way back to their respective ships and, apart from a few legitimate battle scars and monumental hangovers, were none the worse for wear. Inevitably many were faced with the wrath of their Captains at about nine-ish of the clock on the following morning, and expiated their sins by chipping paintwork and scrubbing decks in their spare time, but all were agreed that it had been the mummy and daddy of all runs ashore.

Dusk was beginning to creep across the sea, and the westering sun sent shafting beams across the Atlantic to stretch the shadow of the Rock long to the east as *Caucasian* and her consorts sailed westwards into the Atlantic because the Spanish coast was alive with prying eyes, and all too often the innocent Spanish trawlers carried short-wave radio transmitters.

Two nights later, the moon obscured by heavy cloud, in a rain squall and with a fast eastbound convoy under guard she led her flotilla back through the Straits. To port the darkened, looming bulk of the Rock, to starboard the glittering ribbon of foreshore lights showed where, in uneasy neutrality, lay Tangier: a clearing house for Nazi intelligence, and a hotbed of spies whose duty it was to report the movement of British ships using the Straits. Fishing boats can be accidentally rammed and sunk, but the north coast of Africa was a different matter; subterfuge was, therefore, necessary, and a dark night was a gift from the gods.

Dawn found the convoy and escorts spread out over a wide area so as to make, individually, as small a target as possible. The sun rose brilliantly into a sky as peerless as blue crystal, the sea was as smooth as an inland lake and the ships, bow waves creaming in foaming Vs and with wakes spread in wide peacocks' tails, raced to the east, forcing the pace. A sense of urgency and impending disaster prevailed; anxious eyes swept the horizon for signs of aircraft, and for sign of the telltale wisp of smoke or of enemy fighting tops. Guns were elevated and lowered, and came back to the fore-and-aft position. Firing circuits were tested, and magazines thrown open with the metallic clang of hatch covers which caused everyone to jump. Ships' companies had been closed up at action stations since fifteen minutes before dawn; a routine, a way of life, which they would follow for many months to come.

The Professor, lolling against the mounting of the port after pom-pom, puffed at his cigarette and reflected that the picture postcards did not lie, that the sea and sky really were as blue as they were shown. The sun beat down with an intensity which caused him to perspire profusely, and his clothes and anti-flash gear clung to him with a wet clamminess.

Just before noon a lone aircraft was spotted, far off and low on the horizon. A reconnaissance aircraft? Harbinger of the attack? Guns swivelled to the bearing and men stood ready; aircraft from the carrier *Eagle* made threatening gestures, and the aircraft went away. All remained quiet, and the ships, in attack formation, pressed inexorably eastwards. Suddenly, from out of nowhere it seemed, came the scream of falling bombs, and the seas on the convoy's flank erupted in towers of white foam followed by the dull roar of the explosions. Bombs! But no aircraft! What knavery was this? What new weapon did the Italians have? More bombs, more eruptions, and the whine and scream of their falling rose to a crescendo. Then the aircraft were spotted, high in the sky and almost invisible in the glare of the sun. Anti-aircraft guns barked into the heavens, but the white puffballs of their exploding shells were far short of their targets. The enemy was too high. The bombs fell harmlessly into the sea and, suddenly, it was all over; the Wops had gone home.

Such was to prove the pattern of all Italian air attacks; the planes kept high, well out of range of the anti-aircraft guns, and their bombs were wasted. No ships were hit and the attacks became something of a joke. After the initial tensions of the attacks everyone relaxed a little and had a good laugh at the expense of the Italian air force, and Captains became very proficient at bomb-dodging. A new game was devised, 'Italian skittles' it was called; the rules of the game were to spot the bombs as they were falling – an essential part of the procedure if one was to live to play it – and then put the wheel hard over and dodge 'em. Loud cheers and jeers erupted as the bombs fell harmlessly into the sea. All ships followed the same rules, and the convoy became like a huge draughts board; 'Ther' luv... your move next... oh, well missed, old boy!... now, now, none of yer bodyline stuff, stick to the rules, old thing... oops, dearie, you're getting splashed!' But, for all the macabre humour, it was a game played in deadly earnest.

The action off the coast of Calabria had been a running fight, with the Italian fleet doing the running. The battleship *Giulio Cesare* and the cruiser *Bolzano* – an' bleedin' Bolzano to yew! – were hit, and the remainder headed, in a hurry, for La Spezia, Genoa and points north. Fresh from the action came the Mediterranean Fleet to join forces with the eastbound convoy and to welcome them to the fold. One chummy destroyer made a signal to *Caucasian*: 'Welcome to these Elysian fields.' Commander Philip St John Norton replied: 'Having entered we shall not abandon hope – anything I can do to help?'

The Italian air attacks may have been harmless to the ships. The height from which they bombed was not part of any strategy; they were just too bloody scared to come any closer, but such was not the case with Malta. That luckless island did not respond to helm, and had been subjected to heavy bombing. The islanders and garrison were suffering.

Units of the convoy and escort were detached to enter Grand Harbour. The remainder, mostly warships, steamed on to Alexandria, *Caucasian* with them. Wave after wave of Italian bombers flew over the narrow sea between Sicily and the North African coast and 'bomb alley' as it became known, was a cacophony of noise from falling bombs and barking guns. During the day there was little respite; men spent the hours closed up at action stations and kept the bombers high. From first light to dusk there was always the fear of the bomb which did not miss, and the ever-present threat of surface action. At night came the fitful sleep of fear, as men tossed and turned fully clothed in the stinking humidity of the battened-down messdecks. With watertight doors and hatches closed and clipped to give maximum security, and anti-flash screens rigged, the ships were at a first degree of readiness the whole time. By day and night the 'tween decks were stifling and airless; for obvious reasons men preferred the upper deck, and some, using duffle coats for blankets, preferred to sleep up there.

War burst upon the sweltering deserts of North Africa even as the ships neared Alexandria, and the Desert Army of General Wavell prepared to defend to the death the vital lifeline of the Suez Canal. Despite the imminence of air attacks the ship's company was fallen in at Stations for Entering Harbour. Even those who had no Harbour Stations found one and gaped like a bunch of tourists, wide-eyed and excited at the prospect which lay before their eyes. Here were fresh fields to conquer. Here was romance and high adventure in the land of the Ptolemies, of Alexander, and of Antony and Cleopatra; a country of legend and myth, a country old and in decline before the Briton emerged from his cave. Past the spot where once had stood that wonder of the ancient world, the Pharos lighthouse, over waters that had known the caress of the felucca's keel for a thousand years before the birth of Christ. The ship went to anchor in the middle of the harbour, went about the business of securing from the sea, and the hands returned to gape.

Traders, invaders, and refugees had gaped before. Israelite, Muslim and Christian and people from all the nations of the world had gazed upon this white-painted, shimmering city of dreaming domes and slender minarets; albeit it was somewhat despoiled by coalbunkers, derrick jibs, and factory chimneys, but romantic ne'ertheless. In this gateway to the east they gazed with wonder in their eyes, and the evocative scents of the Orient in their nostrils. These white sea-encroached walls had resounded to the roar of Nelson's cannon at Aboukir Bay, and to the beat of the corsair's tom-tom and the crack of the slave-driver's whip as sweating, cursing, hope-abandoned galley slaves bent to their oars, or slumped, beaten to death across the rower's bench. Such tales could these walls tell.

The inherent trading instincts of the Alexandrians brought them out in their droves to the incoming ships, sailing their handy little feluccas with all the panache of Cowes yachtsmen, and shouting their greetings and hawking their wares around the fleet as they have done from time immemorial. In their long, flowing robes and baggy trousers, and wearing the tarboosh upon their heads like a badge of office, they epitomized the very essence of eastern promise. It was all part of the game, the props of the stage production; on occasions like this, when there were sheep for the shearing, they abandoned their smart European lounge suits and went 'native'. It paid better that way. Allah the almighty, the all-seeing; Allah the wise in his wisdom, had ceased to send the great, white ships of the tourist and eastern trade to the port of Alexandria, but he had, in his mercy and goodness, sent the infidel sailors in great, grey ships in their stead. All praise be to Allah; Allah the provider, the protector of trade, Y'Allah! Allah be praised.

As the day had yet to come when the traders would be barred from HM ships, they were permitted by a tolerant authority to open shop in the waist (amidships) of *Caucasian*; and such a bartering and a buying there was; such a thieving and a swindling. For hours they bartered. Both sides begged, swore, abused, stole and flattered. Jack was determined not to be robbed. For precisely the same reason the wily oriental gentlemen were equally determined, and both parties entered the lists with gusto. A variety of knickknacks, from beads and bangles to souvenirs of Alexandria and items of utilitarian value, were spirited away for'ard; a meaningful nod from the trader to his urchin assistant – an apprentice to the trade of daylight robbery without violence – and the items were retrieved from the empty messdecks and restored to the market-place with a stealth and craftiness equal to that employed when the articles were first misplaced. Not only did the urchins retrieve the misplaced property, but also any items and fittings of a portable nature which happened to be lying around. The Chief Yeoman of Signals thought that he would keep a weather eye on the ensign fluttering proudly from the jackstaff: 'Jest in case some thievin' bastard took a shine to that!'

There was offered merchandise of special attraction to the 'ladees baack 'ome'. There were highly ornate leather handbags, Persian slippers with turned-up toes, purses, and the most immaculate, most superlative, genuine hide (but more likely cardboard) suitcases in which to put everything purchased or misplaced.

Suddenly across the harbour came the portentous wail of the air raid sirens and in almost the same instant the ship's action klaxon sounded. Within seconds action stations were manned and the ship cleared of traders who, scattering like the sands of the desert before the sirocco, grabbed their belongings and piled into their feluccas and headed shoreward fast. Ships which fired guns were not places where any self-respecting Arab trading gentleman would be found dead. Seconds later all hell broke loose, bombs whistled down and flak went up from every ship in the harbour. Meanwhile with every stitch of canvas stretched to the Levantine winds, the traders in their stern sheets knelt in prayer to Allah. Allah the all-seeing, the merciful. Allah the protector of poor honest traders, the diverter of bombs. But Allah in his infinite wisdom heeded not the supplications of the faithful and, with a roar and a cloud of smoke, half a dozen feluccas were blasted into eternity and the Mohammedan hereafter.

Panic gripped the teeming streets and alleyways of the ancient city; houses disappeared in billows of dust, smoke and flying debris. The native population milled around in frightened, aimless chaos, but there was nowhere for them to run for shelter. They screamed, shouted, and blubbered in demented fright; cowered in doorways, down alleyways, and under their robes in the open streets. They fought, cursed, and looted, and called upon Allah for his mercy and protection. But there was no protection, not in the city anyway. Their only protection lay at anchor in the harbour, and in the desert beyond the city where the gunners, stripped to the waist, toiled at their guns.

It was a haphazard raid, carried through with the usual Italian lack of resolution; it soon passed and life returned to normal – the local populace could not permit even the Italian Air Force to interfere with trade for too long.

From the ships came the sailors for a few well earned hours of shore leave, one watch at a time; one watch ashore, one watch aboard to man the guns if the Italian Air Force returned. It was only a few hours' leave to each watch each day, and all leave expired at four bells in the second dogwatch (6 p.m.).

Resplendent in full white uniform, or starched and pressed white tropical shirt and shorts, Jack combed the city from end to end in search of the good life and, as was ever thus, he turned up in all the wrong places; or, dependent upon how these matters are viewed, all the right places. Jack, the incorrigible ambassador of the British way of life, has a knack for finding his way around, and to put a place out of bounds is tantamount to issuing him with an invitation to go there. All the knavery of the Arabs of Alexandria, or the fury of the Axis, could not keep him from ' 'avin' a good ol' shuftee' (look), or cheat him of the opportunity to stretch his legs on decks which did not constantly roll, or from filling his lungs with the atmosphere of the place.

Alexandria suffered surprisingly little from the Italian air raids; His Majesty's Ships not at all. The Italian airmen were the least aggressive of fighters; despite Mussolini's threats and fist waving they were loath to come too close and, since the RAF had bombed Turin, the *Regia Aeronautica* seemed even less disposed to press the advantage they obviously possessed. It was not the Italians the men of the Mediterannean Fleet were worried about; the major worry was caused by the uncertainty of not knowing how long it would be before the German wolf lost patience with the Italian jackal and came down to the Levant to take a hand himself. These were uneasy days; the spirit was going out of ship's companies; the weeks of waiting for God alone knew what was demoralizing. And to make matters worse the mail from home was erratic to say the least; letters, when they did arrive, having come around the Cape of Good Hope, were as much as two months old.

Occasionally good news filtered through to lift the gloom. The messdecks roared with laughter and cheered the news that the little British trawler *Moonstone* had captured single-handed the *Galileo Galilei*, one of Italy's most powerful submarines and holder of an illustrious name, but precursor of the ignoble end of a navy which possessed some of the world's finest ships but not the men to steam them into action. Neither men nor ships were ever to prove themselves in battle. When news came that the Australian cruiser *Sydney* and her attendant destroyers had sunk the powerful Italian cruiser *Bartolomeo Colleoni* off the coast of Crete the cheers were even louder; another fillip for the British Mediterannean Fleet, and still no British casualties. But, always there, underlying everyone's thoughts, was the threat of the *Luftwaffe*.

Chapter 5

Matapan

'Time, I hope, indeed have no doubt,
will crown our zealous efforts with success.
We are but few, but of the right sort.'

Captain Horatio Nelson to his wife. 16 April, 1794.

Unexpectedly, though long expected, *Caucasian* was ordered to short notice for steam, and her company welcomed the renewed activity. Something to do at last; some job or other coming up. It might mean a fight, but even that was better than swinging around the buoy in this hellhole.

It was a patrol and the first of many. In the weeks that followed *Caucasian* was at sea continuously. Something else to bellyache about. She patrolled the basin of the eastern Mediterranean from Alexandria in the south to the Aegean Islands in the north, 'always tricky them damned islands; a ship could take to the ground there easy enough,' and from the coast of Samaria in the east to the Gulf of Sirte in the west. Always nosing around, always poking about, but there was not much to see. The Italians stayed away; either because they did not relish the chance of action, or because they considered this lonely patrolling destroyer a waste of bombs. The other ships of the fleet seemed to get all the luck. Day after day they went 'duck shooting' in the Sicilian Narrows or chasing units of the Italian Fleet up the coast of Italy. But after a while even that business petered out; the Italian troop transports decided that the Italian Army could get along quite nicely without them, thank you. Or was it the Italian Army who decided against the transports? Whichever way it was, it was a bloody deadly war! The lull before the storm, 'but jest yew wait 'til bleedin' Jerry gets yer – Christ! Yew should 'ave seen the bastards in Norway!'

Caucasian was back in Alexandria, 'stinkin' 'ole! Wot, no bloody mail again? Yer, Jan boy, yew 'eard the buzz? – two bottles uv beer a man – in that bleedin' canteen – rationing the bloody stuff! Christ, wot a bleedin' war!' Two days later they went to sea again, 'no bleedin' rest for the wicked!' But this time things were different, this was no lone patrol, this time the whole Fleet put to sea. *Warspite*, wearing the flag of the Commander-in-Chief, *Valiant*, *Barham*, *Ajax*, *York*, *Sydney*, and *Southampton*, with the destroyer flotillas fanning out on all sides to screen them; and, wallowing in the wake of the big ships, came the monitor, *Terror*, with her huge 16-inch guns. Something, it appeared, was very definitely up.

Four sister destroyers were detached in company with *Caucasian* and, with the latter leading, they followed *Ajax*, *York*, *Sydney*, *Southampton* and *Terror* out of line, reformed into battle formation and steamed to the west. 'Wot's the bleedin' buzz, Jan boy? – wer' we goin' too? – bloody great monitor along, too – must be a bombardment!' It was, the first of many *Caucasian* would take part in; just one of many the Fleet had already done.

Ships manoeuvred in the night, men stood to their action stations in mute expectancy and strained their eyes into the still, deathly hush of sea and night-darkened sky; the only sound was the swish of water down the ship's side and the subdued throb of her engines. *Caucasian* came about in a turn to the south, then west again, and faintly away to port could be discerned a long strip of deeper darkness where lay the coast of Cyrenaica and the road which led west to Benghazi and Tripoli; here also lay the Italian oil storage depots and ammunition dumps. Across the stillness of the night came faintly, muted and vibrating like the sound of dinner gongs, the sound of firing circuits being tested in the big ships. The stillness was almost tangible when, in an instant, the movement-concealing cloud bank shifted and the night sky became moon-ridden and bright with stars; with an even greater suddenness, the whole universe seemed to erupt with a flash and a roar; the bombardment had started, and to the men of *Caucasian*, gaping into the night, there came wafting across the water the acrid smell of spent cordite. 'Christ! – what a bleedin' row! – wouldn't like to be on the receiving end uv that lot, eh Jan boy?' With an uncanny, diminishing whine, sounding like bombs going back up from whence they came, ton after ton of high explosive went hurtling shoreward, and Derna was reduced to rubble. *Caucasian* and her consorts steamed slowly back and forth, east to west and west to east, as they patrolled the outer seaward defence screen. The Italians had a fleet of surface ships, submarines also and fast torpedo boats; there was little chance of interference from either, but no chances were taken.

Meanwhile, far to the west, the ships of Force H from Gibraltar were pushing another convoy through to Malta, and the bombarding ships, except *Terror* and a couple of escorts, would rendezvous with them for the final stage of the run through to Alexandria.

On *Caucasian*'s port after pom-pom the Professor watched the bombardment with awe. Such fury unleashed; such havoc wrought. The Professor was leaning against the gunshield talking to the gun layer, Able Seaman George 'General' Gordon, who sat just inside the shield reclining in the layer's chair.

'Rough luck, "General",' the Professor responded in reply to a tale of woe which he had heard, as indeed had everyone else in the ship, at least a dozen times.

'Rough luck my ass!' spat the worthy 'General', slamming the breach shut with a dull thud; 'I'll give the bitch rough luck; when I gets 'ome I'll break 'er fuckin' neck!'

The 'General's' wife had run off with another man, a foreman in the Royal Ordnance factory where she worked. She had been very nice about it; she had written to the 'General' and told him straight. Her pregnancy, by the foreman, was as good an excuse as any for ending a match which right from the start had been an unfortunate mistake, she said. The foreman was a very nice man, he had promised to do the right thing by her and she was sure the 'General' would understand and do the right thing by giving her a divorce.

'I'll marry the bastards!' the 'General' frothed, 'I'll murder the dirty whore! Fancy that, eight years married, two kids, an' no bleedin' more she sez – an' off she goes an' gets 'erself stuck in the spud line! I'll get leave, that's wot I'll do – I'll see the ol' man an' go 'ome – I'll beat 'er bleedin' 'ead in, – I'll swing fer them bastards yet!'

The 'General' had been frothing at the mouth for a week. One of the few letters to come aboard had contained the news, and he was threatening to see everyone, from the Commander-in-Chief downwards. But all he had so far done was to rage impotently. There was nothing much he could do; to go home was out of the question; the only way out of the Mediterranean Fleet was to leave stitched up in a bolt of canvas, weighted down with a couple of shell cases, draped about with the White Ensign, and dumped overboard one evening at sundown.

The mail had also brought news that one or two members of the ship's company had become fathers, legitimately, since the ship had left the United Kingdom. The babies' heads had been well and truly wetted; the infants being launched upon the sea of life in true nautical fashion over the rum fanny at about eleven bells of the forenoon watch, or at whatever hour the *Regia Aeronautica* had permitted the spirit of Nelson to rise from out the enfolding shrouds of 'Jack Dusty's' (Stores Assistant) spirit room. War or no war, 'Up spirits, stand fast the Holy Ghost' was still the pipe. One enterprising father had approached the Captain, through the proper channels of course, for compassionate leave. In manner both patient and kindly the Captain had pointed out that although the man's presence was essential at the laying down of the keel, he hoped he, the Captain, felt as in fact had so often been proved to be the case, that his presence was not necessary at the launching or, indeed, at the subsequent fitting out. Furthermore, if leave was granted, how did he, the applicant, propose to get home? Between Alexandria and the city of Bristol lay four thousand miles of hostile sea in one direction, sixteen thousand miles around the Cape of Good Hope in the other and, by the only other route, circumnavigation of the earth, twenty-six thousand miles. 'Request not granted – salute the Captain – hayboutturn – doublehawaysmartly!'

From Derna back to Alexandria; a fast run in with the rest of the Fleet and a fast merchantman which had come through from Gibraltar. From Alex the whole flotilla, with *Caucasian* leading, returned to the patrol area off Crete and southern Greece, with forays into the Dodecanese and the Aegean. These were tight waters, and Italian troops were moving upon the mainland of Greece. The Germans were in the Balkans and going east. 'Drang nach Osten' via the Bosphorus and Turkey, or Greece and the Suez Canal? Everyone waited, and feared the waiting.

The Italians still refused to make a fight of it, but the threat was always there. Their air force ranged the skies unmolested, the ships were subjected to incessant high-level bombing and always there was fear of the coming of the Germans. There was the occasional run in with Italian torpedo boats, but such attacks were never pressed home with any resolution, and always ended with the Italians hotfooting it for Taranto, Bari and other points of safety. There was an eagerness to have a crack at the Italian Navy and have done with it.

Week after weary week passed. Dawn and dusk action stations every day, seven days a week. False alarms and aircraft warnings kept everyone on the jump all day and every day. At night the humid, foul-smelling messdecks; and everyone always fully clothed. It was forbidden to undress or even to take a bath. The dhobi-ing sessions were but a shadow of what they had been; men took their dhobi-ing to their action stations these days, and had a quick rub out between air attacks. How they missed the body-washing, soul-cleansing, lung-expanding freedom of the bathroom. A man dare not undress; one of those high-level bombs might not miss, or the fighting tops of the Italian fleet might appear over the horizon. Flash from gunfire and exploding bombs can strip the flesh from the body of an improperly dressed man. Bathing was a luxury reserved for the comparative safety of Alexandria harbour, and even there the bathroom 'sod's opera' was silent. Men had nothing to sing about these days.

Strain was beginning to show in men's faces, and in their demeanour. From the messdecks there came no more the sounds of horseplay and high spirits. Who cared any more whether or not there were ponies down coal mines, or eggs in the crow's nest, or whether the 'golden rivet' was still in place? 'Right down in the bilges, me 'andsome – bend down an' 'ave a look, but make sure yew keeps yer ass ta the bulkhead when yew do!'

The one place in the Mediterranean where the Italians were warlike was in the skies over and in the waters around Malta. Here the bombing was incessant, and here came *Caucasian* with supplies for the island; here the soul-destroying judder of the pom-poms and the crack and whap of the heavier ack-ack beat like mortal blows into a man's head and reduced his mind to a jelly of fear and apprehension. The ship suffered many near misses, which sent showers of water cascading over her decks as she weaved and veered crazily to port or starboard to dodge the bombs. Not that the Italians had grown braver; it was just that there were more of them, and they were operating on their own doorstep.

Food was not all it could have been; corned beef and hardtack were commonplace. Big ships were always a welcome sight; not only for the protection they offered, but because of the fresh bread they baked and the potatoes they carried; both items were fast becoming luxury foods. The sort of luxury that made life that much easier to support, and to make the war seem that much further away. Such luxuries were symbolic; they were more than just bread and spuds, they were the tangible proof, like the mail, of Britain's power to keep the seas; they were the yardstick by which men judged their isolation. Time was when Jack used to complain bitterly when these things ran short, or the mail failed to arrive, but now he merely turned away and said nothing. What the Italians had failed to do by aggression, the combined Axis powers were now achieving by psychology, albeit not consciously employed.

As the Professor lounged around the gun deck during the quiet periods, gazing through the gunsight or desultorily oiling the breechblocks during these weary weeks, he asked himself what was the point of it all – why war? It was all so senseless, so stupid, so shortsighted, so unnecessary. Where were men going? Men who prided themselves on their intellectual achievements in all spheres of human activity have asked themselves these questions since the dawn of time, and yet were still unable to resolve the problems of peaceful coexistence.

The narrow seas between Sicily and the North African coast erupted in towers of white water, the postcard blue of the sky was dotted with the white thistledown puffs of exploding ack-ack shells which floated gossamer-like on the light Mediterranean airs and carried away. So beautiful if it had been a natural phenomenon, but it was not; man fought man on these ancient seas and in these immortal skies, and the convoy went through the Straits. *Barham*, *Berwick* and *Glasgow* with attendant destroyers reached Alexandria two days later, and with an abiding sense of relief *Caucasian*'s ship's company secured from sea; at least one could get a few days' rest in Alex. Now that General Wavell and his merry men had pushed them back to Benghazi and beyond, the Italians had stopped coming so far away from home; fighting those nasty Tommies was far too risky, and for the first time in months Alexandria became a veritable haven of peace for war-weary sailors, without bombs and with the war but a distant rumble up the desert.

The main off-duty occupations of the British sailors were dhobi-ing, writing letters home and sleeping the sleep of the utterly exhausted. The ships which had just been brought through the narrows had delivered the latest mail, a mere six weeks old. The standard of food improved, as it always did in harbour, and an air of normality returned.

The morning after *Caucasian*'s arrival 'Sludge' Coles came up to where Johnny Thomas and the Professor were wielding not very energetic paintbrushes up the for'ard funnel; near misses had played havoc with the paintwork.

'Hi, Prof!' he yelled up the funnel to where the pair sat suspended on a stage. 'The ol' man wants ta see ya in 'is cabin – at the dip!' (quickly).

Five minutes later the Professor was back.

The look in his eyes, and the expression on his face, choked the query in Thomas's throat. For a long time the Professor did not speak; he just stood with blind, all-seeing eyes and gazed out across the harbour. Johnny said nothing; instinctively he knew that there was nothing he could say.

'Mum and Dad are dead, Johnny; air raid.'

Just that and no more. With pity in his eyes, Johnny stood mute, a helpless look on his face. What did a bloke say when things like this happened? There was nothing he could say, nothing anyone could say, nothing that would make the slightest difference. Mutely the Professor turned and walked away, and Johnny returned to his red-lead brush.

Half an hour later his bereaved friend returned. 'Righto, Tomo – knockit off, stand easy, tea's brewed – I've just made it'.

So passed the Professor's parents, and from that day on the matter was never raised again. The look in his eyes spoke of unmitigated grief, and that is something one bears alone. A pat on the back and a gruff 'Rough luck, Prof ' and the rest of the ship's company respected his grief.

Balmy raider-free sky and comparative peace did a little to restore the spirits of the men of *Caucasian*; a man could even sleep at night with the portholes open and the ventilation switched on, but the restful days were lived against a backdrop of increasing enemy activity. Malta, from her isolation within enemy-dominated territory, was getting desperate for supplies and yet again *Caucasian*, in company with the entire Mediterranean Fleet, put to sea in an endeavour to break the enemy stranglehold, and as they went the raiders returned to Alexandria, this time with a dual purpose, with the Fleet as a target, and as a diversion to cover the invasion of Greece.

Pressing forward at maximum speed and loaded with supplies for the beleaguered island, the ships beat off the attackers and steamed to the west. From Gibraltar came Force H, covering a convoy of fast merchantmen, and steaming east. Attack followed attack, and from dawn to dusk the sky was rent by the sound of battle. Men toiled and sweated at the guns, hungry, dirty, and up to their knees in spent shell cases. The only relief came at night, but such relief was only partial; always there was the threat of Italian submarines, of U-Boats, known to be in these waters, E-Boats, and the ever-present uncertainty about the Italian Fleet. The hours of darkness were fraught with danger, and were but an uneasy relief from the greater perils of the day. In the absence of accurate information about the enemy's movements dawn could easily find both fleets face to face. Experience had shown that thc Italians invariably ran away, but cvcn a running fight could inflict damage and sudden death. The dawns were still, hushed with expectancy, and as the sun crept over the eastern horizon, filled with straining eyes.

Among the men who fought the ships of the Middle Eastern Fleet a new phrase was creeping into usage: 'bomb-happy'. Even the snotty-nosed, bleary-eyed, 'Tosh' Harding, Chief Yeoman of Signals, was no longer suffering from the 'screaming abdabs', he was bomb-happy; 'Ain't I got a fuckin' right ta be bleedin' well bomb-'appy – first *Courageous*, then soddin' Norway – an' now this – bleedin' lot – 'snuff ta make any bastard bomb-'appy!' And so it was. Bomb-happiness kept a man awake at night, and in severe cases kept him on deck every minute of every twenty-four hours because he was too scared to go below. In his imagination he heard the crash and roar of the bomb which hit the ship, and saw the 'tween decks rent asunder into a mass of twisted body-maiming metal; heard the ship's sides splitting and saw the horror of the inrushing sea. He was trapped below decks, fighting for his life in a sinking steel prison from which there was no escape, and he awoke screaming and fighting for breath, his body in a cold sweat, and his limbs trembling.

In the ships the guns were red-hot; the screaming whine of falling bombs and the traumatic judder of the pom-poms beat an unholy tattoo; *Caucasian* shook from stem to stern under the violence and demoniac pounding of war as, time after time, she heeled over to the force of near misses. The acrid stench of spent cordite pervaded the shimmering air, men slipped on the steel deck plates as they fought to stay upright every time the ship heeled over, and they sweated with the heat and fear of the bomb which might not miss.

Malta appeared over the western horizon, a heat-shimmering mirage on a sun-drenched sea. As the ships drew nearer it was seen that the island was erupting like a seagirt volcano; line after line of tracer skeined into the cloudless sky, and the sound of the crump and roar of exploding bombs carried across the sea to the approaching ships. Grand Harbour was a holocaust of noise, smoke and clouds of swirling dust. The ancient walls of the crusaders' fortresses of Valletta, Senglea, Kalafrana, and St Angelo reverberated to the noise of battle, and from every quarter the guns of the defenders spat defiance. Those guns grew so hot that they often seized up, with disastrous consequences for their crews, and as happened too often those crews knew the bitter chagrin of silence brought about by lack of ammunition. It was to feed these guns and the men who manned them, to succour the civilian population, and to bring replacements for the men who had died in the island's defence, that the ships had fought their way through from Alexandria, from Gibraltar, and before that through the U-Boat-infested North Atlantic.

To take replacements alongside for disembarkation, to provide additional anti-aircraft coverage for the quick turnaround of the ships, and to bring out the 'empties', the destroyers fought their way into Grand Harbour in line ahead, every gun blazing. The historic harbour was a shambles. Here was damage beyond the wildest dreams of crusading knight or rapacious Moor; here was being written the darkest page in the island's turbulent history. Some of the island's inhabitants who had found refuge in the caves and dark underground places ventured a peep at the incoming ships and a ragged little cheer was raised.

Gone was the gaiety and garrulous bustle of peacetime Malta; the dhaigsas (dai-sos) and their vociferous oarsman were gone into retirement for the duration, and the chattering women and their hordes of noisy, ragged urchins were absent from the many quays and waterfront lidos. The hundreds of waterfront bars which had solely existed to cater for the needs of Jolly Jack were all closed down; deserted and empty shells or heaps of rubble. Here, in the happy days just before the war, a sailor could get steak, egg, and chips, a belly full of beer, and a night's sleep for a few shillings in one of the numerous 'all night inners' and, if he was broke, it went on the slate until pay-day. The Ramillies Bar, The Barham Bar, The Valiant Bar, The Resolution Bar were all named after ships of the Fleet, and if Jack would slake his thirst in places which did not remind him of the ship in which he served there was The Friendly Bar, The Friend to All Bar, The Lucky Strike Bar, The Home from Home Bar, and The Cricketer's Arms. The bars had been legion, all designed to exert nostalgic appeal on Jack. Each ship in the Fleet had its own favourite bar, and woe betide the interlopers from other ships. The famous 'Gut', from its former glory of dosshouses, honky-tonks, eating places, and quarter mile of nautical battleground, was now a street of ghosts. Not even the scrawny alley cats were there to rummage the now non-existent garbage cans; alley cats and the contents of garbage cans, both being edible, were in short supply.

Grand Harbour is like a cauldron, hemmed in on three sides by massive bastions and houses in steeply-rising streets. How the Italians could fail to hit the ships was hard to understand; but fail they did; cowardice and the heavy ack-ack barrage kept them high, and with only superficial damage the ships cleared harbour and ran for Alexandria.

The weeks that followed saw *Caucasian* and the rest of the Fleet running non-stop with supplies and troops for Greece, to counter the invasion of that country. Convoys to Greece, incessant patrols, bombardments of the enemy coast, and the occasional long-distance sighting of the Italian Fleet kept men and ships working until they almost reached breaking point. *Ajax* and *York* managed to trap enemy destroyers and sink them in a gun action. *Caucasian* shot a fast torpedo boat out of the water in a lightning gun action off the western Peloponnese, and she also put ashore on the Albanian coast a strange, bearded gentleman who wore a deerstalker hat and carried a rolled umbrella.

On the evening of 11 November *Caucasian* found herself in company with other destroyers acting as close escort to the newly arrived aircraft carrier *Illustrious*.

Across the moonlit water *Illustrious* could be seen steaming into the wind to get her aircraft off, and across the intervening sea came faintly the roar of the engines as one after the other the aircraft cleared the flight deck and winged into the night.

'Some bastard's in fer a nasty shock!' In the darkness, in the lee of the gun shield, 'General' Gordon chuckled with relish and expressed the sentiments of everyone on deck. Away to the north-west at Taranto pandemonium reigned; a right merry tune was played in the Mar Grande and Mar Piccolo as the Italian Fleet reeled from the shock of the hard-pressed torpedo attack. During the period of waiting for the aircraft to return to the carrier *Caucasian* had occasion to steam alongside her huge companion of the night. Looming like an immense moon-illuminated argosy she made those in the little destroyer feel very small and vulnerable.

'Shouldn't like to be aboard that bastard,' said the 'General' looking up at the towering hulk. 'Must be like a bleedin', floatin' barracks – too bloody big – too bloody easy to 'it.' It was not to be long before the 'General's' prophetic pessimism was proved correct, and there was enacted one of the greatest epics in British Naval history. The destroyers' responsibility was great; they were guarding something very special, the carrier's value to the Fleet was incalculable. Eyes peered into the darkness, and every nerve was on the alert for anything amiss; a U-Boat or an E-Boat, especially the fast torpedo carriers, could do untold damage to the great, vulnerable carrier. But nothing special happened; the aircraft were landed on and, at a top speed of some thirty knots, the striking force formed up and headed for Alexandria – the more distance they could put between themselves and the heel of Italy between now and daylight the better. That the raiders would come again at dawn, to wreak a terrible vengeance for the night's work, no one doubted. 'So flash 'er up, "Stokes", and let's get to hell outa here!'

Their frothing phosphorescent wakes denoting the measure of their hurry, carrier and escorts cleaved through the night, and dawn found them far to the south and east and closed up at action stations. Signal lamps winked as the dawn grew into day, and the news of the night's success sent the men of *Caucasian* into an ecstasy of joy; they cheered, whooped, clapped each other on the back, and generally and noisily agreed that their's was a bloody fine Navy. 'Good ol' Fleet Air Arm! Good ol' Jack! We showed the bastards!' As the news flashed around the Fleet it was learned that three battleships had been sunk or damaged, a cruiser and some destroyers hit, and severe damage done to the dockyard. The news was like a tonic. Hope flickered anew and tired men grew strong and tall. 'Stripey' Ackers, at about eleven bells-ish in the forenoon watch, when the spirit of Nelson rose with an approving nod, instead of his usual toast to the nautical vices, raised his glass to the light and said, 'Gen'lemen I gives yew a toast – to the Fleet Air Arm. God bless 'em!'

Week followed week and the grinding routine of eat, sleep, and action stations continued unabated. There was another brush with the Italian Fleet; a running fight as usual, with Italian shirt-tails flapping to the crack of British guns. Christmas came and went almost without notice. As the dawn of Christmas Day stole from out of the east, from the land of Judaea, its evocative glow found *Caucasian* in the Dodecanese with the hands closed up at action stations. To the accompaniment of a harmonica, ably assisted by paper and comb, there had been the singing of carols on the messdeck the previous evening. Christmas morning prayers had been led by the Captain; more carols, a few well-chosen words, and the service ended with that lusty, lung-swelling and poignant hymn beloved of all sailors: 'Eternal Father, strong to save.'

'Oh hear us when we cry to thee
For those in peril on the sea.'

Nostalgia ruled the ritual of the rum fanny. Men stood silent, and 'Stripey' Ackers struck responsive chords when, squinting solemnly at his tot held at arm's length to the electric light bulb in the approved manner, he uttered his usual benediction for the further enlightenment of the unwashed and ungodly: 'Not a bad drop o' bubbly that! Gen'elmen, I gives yew a toast', he paused for effect, gazed solemnly around at his assembled messmates, and said: 'To them wot waits at 'ome – may God bless 'em an' keep 'em safe.'

'May God bless 'em an' keep 'em safe,' the gathering responded.

The year came to an end and she was back in Alexandria; the old year went out and its passing was hardly noticed; the new year was celebrated hardly at all. Fateful 1941 dawned with Levantine brilliance, and there was hope in the Fleet; the Greeks had the Italians on the run; in the desert General Wavell was pushing them ever westward, and upon the sea the Royal Navy yet reigned supreme.

On the sixth day of the first month of this terrible year the Fleet sailed from Alexandria: it was a big job; the entire Fleet steamed to the west, and there were supply ships in company. Malta again. Into the Sicilian narrows, and the ships from Alex took over the convoy from Force H under Admiral Somerville from Gibraltar. At this juncture the relieving ships turned and headed back for the further relief of the beleaguered island. An air of nervous apprehension hung over the Fleet like the muffling folds of a blanket.

The Fleet had been shadowed ever since it had left Alexandria. Far out and low down on the horizon the enemy aircraft had flown their spying missions; always too far away to get at, even for the aircraft from *Illustrious* and *Eagle*. Men fretted, watched, and waited; nearly every ship in the Mediterranean Fleet was in the narrows; surely they had a pasting coming today.

At maximum speed Fleet and supply ships pressed on to Malta. *Illustrious* and *Eagle*, with their own protective screen of destroyers; the battleships in line ahead, the cruisers standing off the line, with the supply ships between them and the battle wagons. The destroyers, hull down and knifing the sea into foaming wake, fanned out to form the protective outer screen.

During the afternoon watch of the tenth day of the first month there came a sporadic burst of ack-ack fire from the convoy's northern screen. Ships were already at action stations and the usual air attack developed; high in the sky came the Italian bombers, down came the bombs with a swoosh and a roar, and up went the flak – just to discourage any infringement of the rules by the intrepid Italian pilots. Suddenly the men at the guns, at the directors, and everyone on deck stiffened to attention. Some of the pilots were definitely not playing the game; some of them were actually diving to the attack!

Now laying 'Y' gun, the Professor swung to the bearing given for the attacking planes; squinting through his sights he yelled the repeat of range and bearing, and his sight locked on the diving bombers. Suddenly he let out a howl of consternation: 'Jesus Christ!' he yelled above the din of the screaming bombers, exploding bombs, and vicious whap of gunfire, 'It's Jerry!'

Jerry indeed it was, screaming down out of the afternoon sun, peeling off one after the other, and plummeting upon the ships like black harbingers of death. Attack followed attack, and the umbrella of flak from the defiant ships deterred them not at all. Here were no Italians playing at war. Here were men in deadly earnest, hard-bitten veterans of half-a-dozen campaigns, highly trained killing machines, grim, determined dive-bombing experts; there was no stopping them; they were afraid of nothing that the ships could throw at them. The high-pitched scream of their diving was designed to demoralize, and it went a long way to doing just that. As the realization of all that was portended by the appearance of the dreaded *Luftwaffe* in the central Mediterranean dawned the growing confidence of the last few weeks was shattered in a stroke. These were men to be feared; the scream of their diving aircraft was to be for long the substance of sailors' nightmares. Out of the sun they plummeted like hawks to their prey, only pulling out of their terrifying dives when it appeared that they must surely crash onto the ships which they bombed. On orders from Berlin the *Luftwaffe* had come hunting *Illustrious*.

The Ju 87s and 88s concentrated on the carrier; *Eagle* had already been hit and detached with bomb damage, and she disappeared in a welter of smoke, flame, and high-flung columns of water. Time after time the screaming bombers dived to the attack, and time after time *Illustrious* reeled from repeated hits. In the other ships men watched this terrible punishment with bated breath; flame and smoke belched from her and she staggered drunkenly, out of control. The ships of the escort raced to her aid and with blazing guns tried to beat off her tormentors; but there was no stopping the men of the *Luftwaffe* and, as the planes roared overhead, the pilots could be seen in their cockpits grinning and waving mockingly to the gunners toiling in the ships below.

In *Illustrious* the hangar and 'tween decks became a hell of screaming, shattered men and twisted metal, and only darkness, merciful blessed darkness, saved her from total destruction. She made Malta under her own steam, where dockyard and ship's company worked until they dropped in their endeavours to patch her up and get her back to sea again. But she was not to be allowed to lick her wounds in peace, her tormentors found her where she lay at Parlatoria Wharf in the Grand Harbour and once again she was subjected to attack after attack. The walls of the ancient fortress reverberated to the roar of the dive bomber's engines and the thunder of the guns and exploding bombs; the very air of the cauldron which is Grand Harbour danced to the tune the guns played, and the smell of death and destruction hung heavy in the pall of the smoke of battle. In the ships, in the workshops of the dockyard, and in the deep underground places where people found shelter from the pandemonium which reigned above, men, women, and children knelt and prayed to God to get the luckless carrier repaired and away from the island. Here was man-made fury without precedent in the history of man on earth. Madonna mia! What have we done to be thus tormented? In the deep ways below the earth men shook impotent fists at the masonry above their heads, and the priests comforted the living and administered extreme unction to the dead.

In the ships empty shell cases were strewn over the decks until it became impossible to walk, magazines were emptied, and guns fell silent through lack of ammunition. For thirteen days the battle raged, and on the night of the thirteenth day *Illustrious* was gone; all the extremes of sacrifice, the blood, the sweat, the toil, the tears and the prayers, had not been in vain, and the gallant carrier lived to fight another day. As dusk settled over the narrow sea she cleared for Alexandria and steamed into the protective night, a floating funeral pyre of desperately gallant men and, as she pressed to the east, her heroic handmaidens, the over-worked, hard-pressed, battle-grimed destroyers fanned out in escort and ushered her to safety.

In the night the ships steamed east; ships' companies cleared their decks of the debris of battle, and feared the coming dawn. As the sun began to climb the hill of the eastern sea haggard men closed up at action stations and, if they had any ammunition left, prepared to fight their guns in a last despairing effort to get the stricken carrier through. The atmosphere in the ships was potent with fear and dread; apprehensive eyes searched the slanting rays of the sun and the morning cloud and, with nerves stretched to breaking point and fingers nervously toying with the firing mechanism of the guns, the men of *Caucasian* and her consorts searched the lightening sky for sign of the enemy; but the dive bombers did not come, and *Illustrious* reached Alexandria two days later.

In the eastern Mediterranean the Fleet reeled from the mauling it had received at the hands of the *Luftwaffe*, and there was abroad a very real fear of the morrow. Friend mourned friend, and ship mourned ship. *Illustrious* was not the only casualty of the recent battle; *Southampton* had been sunk, *Gloucester* badly damaged, and there was an accumulation of minor damage to lesser ships. *Caucasian* was dirty and battle-scarred, but otherwise intact, and the same was true of her company. What was true of her was also true of all the other ships, but there was no rest; after taking on stores, fuel, and ammunition, back to sea they went for the build-up to the Battle of Greece. To Suda Bay, to Athens and Piraeus they sailed, in waters immortalized in history. Now once again the men of Britain were back on these famous shores; once again to die in defence of the rights of man.

Even under the duress of war the minds of men can turn to more enduring things. 'Who built that bloody Parthenon, Prof? 'Who wus that bloke 'omer?' 'What about ol' Socrates – wasn't 'e a dirty bastard – got tried fer muckin' about wiv small boys or summat, didn't 'e?' The Professor answered a hundred questions and in a few spare hours led an expedition to the Acropolis. All very cultural and learned, and the sailors trooped about like a bunch of gaping tourists. They enquired, they poked about, and they marvelled at all they saw and heard. Here stood Demosthenes of oratorical perfection; there the place where Socrates might have taught; and here might have been his prison and perhaps there might have stood the cup of hemlock. There the Odeon of Herodes Atticus – all the names, if nothing else, were familiar to devotees of the cinema. And there the Theatre of Dionysus where the fertile imaginations of Sophocles and Euripides revealed the glory of the spoken word to audiences among whom were numbered some of the greatest men of all time. The men of *Caucasian* trod the hallowed ground and talked of the glory that was Greece, and of the missus and kids and the folks back home, and of the war. The Professor answered their questions, sympathized about the missus and kids, but could do nothing about the war, and they all got drunk in the waterfront bars of the Piraeus.

Troops were everywhere, singing, as men always have sung when they march to war; from their tanks and lorries, from their seats on artillery pieces, from their armoured cars and from time-honoured Shanks's pony, they waved to the sailors as they passed and headed for the plains and mountains of the north.

In the back streets of the Piraeus dwelt ladies whose only desire, they claimed, was to cater for the physical well-being of the mighty British sailors, the saviours of Greece. There was a club which specialized in the belly dance, and anyone could get up and have a go; the ladies' navels rotated and contrarotated, and so did the sailors' eyeballs. Ouzo was twopence a pint – aniseed balls again – and the local brew, retsina, was not much more expensive; retsina and ouzo mixed are enough to make any sailor's eyeballs rotate!

Back to Alexandria went *Caucasian*, and then back to Greece; the shuttle service of troops and supplies was maintained around the clock because the situation was fast becoming critical. Malta was being besieged on an unprecedented scale, General Rommel was in the Libyan desert and in the north of Greece the Panzer divisions were massing. The storm clouds gathered and the thunder of war rumbled around the heavens.

The monitor *Terror* was sunk on her way back from bombarding Benghazi. Mines had been laid in the Suez Canal and thus prevented the carrier *Formidable*, so sorely needed to replace the damaged *Illustrious*, from getting through. Ships were now being sunk on the Alexandria–Piraeus run, and the *Luftwaffe* was on the island of Rhodes and in the Dodecanese. There was no way west, and no way east because the Suez Canal was closed; the Mediterranean Fleet was trapped in the basin of the Levant. In the north of Greece the Panzers crossed the border and Mount Grammos echoed to the sounds of war. The local people – Serbs, Croats, Slavs and Bulgars, stood mute and with hatred in their eyes as they watched the hereditary enemy thunder down through Edhessa and out upon the plain of Macedonia; before the advancing army were driven hordes of refugees; men, women and children in black despair, helpless flotsam on the floodtide of war. Behind the refugees, fighting a hopeless rearguard action, came British troops with their allies the Greeks; down through the mountains and across the plain, down past Olympia and through Thermophylae to Levadia and Thebes; in that fateful spring of 1941 it was the British who held the pass and there was no fleet in Phaleron Bay, only a few battle-weary British destroyers manned by men on the verge of cracking up. Action strain was reflected in hollow, sleep-deprived eyes, and etched in the haggard faces of men who never left their action stations. The telltale twitch of facial muscles, the nervous blinking eyes; everyone was bomb-happy.

In *Caucasian* 'Tosh' Harding paced the flag deck, nervously scanned the sky with his binoculars and kept a watchful eye for the blink of Aldis lamps from other ships. The Captain, sitting in his high chair behind the binnacle, watched 'Tosh' from the corner of his eye. Harding was cracking up. The First Lieutenant watched the Captain, noted the spate of new lines in the old man's face, and saw bright, feverish eyes. The Captain had recently noticed that the First Lieutenant had developed a habit of wringing his hands. From the Captain down the strain was telling in a hundred different ways; on the messdecks rum was a panacea and was issued at the end of each day, at a time when there was least likelihood of attack; it helped a man to sleep.

The time between attacks were the worst; times when a man had time to stop and think, and wait for the next attack. During the actual fighting he was too damned busy to think; too damned busy, and too damned scared. Yet fear played no visible part of life in *Caucasian*; fear was a personal thing with which a man wrestled alone and in the dark. The greatest fear was fear of showing fear; every man was a hero to his neighbour. When the dive bombers screamed from out the sky the man who knew no fear was either a fool or his life had little meaning. At times like these the Professor's belly crawled with dread, his heart came up into his mouth and beat until he was conscious of its beating. But he was not afraid, he tried to convince himself; or was he? How does a man recognize fear? What was this sensation in the stomach and in the heart, this constriction in the chest, if not fear? Suppose he got blasted to kingdom come. What then? Was he afraid to die, afraid of the hereafter, afraid to face his God? What God? Was there a God who sat back and watched this carnage, this hell on earth? The Professor tried to analyse the anatomy of fear, and told himself, as he had done so many times over these last few months, that he could not; all he really knew was that he was scared to bloody death.

Another convoy was pushed through to Malta and, despite the *Luftwaffe*, part of it got through; but the strain on men and ships was terrible, bringing both almost to breaking point. Ships were long overdue for refit, and only superhuman effort kept them going. Day after day the bombers came, dawn to dusk, seven days a week. Grand Harbour was untenable, and warships were too precious to risk in its narrow confines; so, whilst the escorts swept the sea to the north and east hoping for an encounter with the Italian Navy, the merchantmen went in alone to unload their precious cargoes. The great fear was that the Italian Fleet might put to sea with German crews and, if that happened, the consequences were too frightful to contemplate.

Towards the end of March *Caucasian* was ordered, with her flotilla, to patrol to the west of Crete, the destroyers joining the cruisers *Orion*, *Ajax*, *Perth* and *Gloucester*. The Italian Fleet was out in force, it was learned, and the British ships were looking for them. They rendezvoused to the south-west of Gavhdos Island.

All through the day the tension mounted, and there was no sign of the enemy; then, just after dawn the next day, the eyes of the British Fleet sighted smoke and the mastheads of fighting ships; ships which were in the wrong place to be friendly. The cry was raised and, despite the fact that everyone was closed up at action stations, the action klaxons sounded; it turned out to be a small force of Italian cruisers and destroyers and, acting on orders, the British ships turned away. Shortly afterwards everyone was galvanized into action again, guns swung to the new bearing, and everyone stood to as the fighting tops of two Italian battleships broke the horizon to the north. In the British ships men held their breath as they waited for the Italians' heavy guns to open up, but they failed to do so and the British ships turned away under cover of heavy smoke. Huge clouds of heavy, sulphurous smoke poured from the speeding destroyers; men coughed and their eyes smarted in the gloom and fouled air, faces blackened and, as the ships turned into their own smoke, the position was not a healthy one. To starboard the enemy lurked behind the British smoke screen, and to port steamed the enemy battleships, and no one knew how many escorts. The smoke obscured the picture, and at noon a further force of enemy battleships were reported to the south.

'Jesus Christ!' exclaimed the 'General' as the news was relayed from *Caucasian*'s bridge, 'we'm in a bleedin' box an' no mistake – 'ope Andy bleedin' Cunningham knows wot 'es about – if 'e don't fuckin' well 'urry up, we've 'ad it!'

The Italians opened fire at extreme range, and the shells fell short; but, as the range closed, shells screamed over the mastheads of the British ships.

' 'Ere they come!' screamed the 'General', ' 'bout bleedin' time too – loafin' showera bastards – baggin' orf (wenching) in Alex, I 'spect, whilst us poor buggers ploughs the bleedin' 'og's wash (sea)!' The 'General's' remarks were addressed to the British battle squadron which had appeared over the horizon to the south. Aircraft from the carrier *Formidable* flew overhead to attack the Italian ships, and their appearance was greeted with a ragged cheer.

'Takes me 'at orf ta them bastards!' the 'General' nodded to where the strike aircraft of the Fleet Air Arm were attacking the enemy ships. 'Bloody good job they showed up – an' not before time neiver!'

By mid-afternoon it became clear that the Italians were not going to fight; they were steaming north-west towards home at a speed of knots, and it also became obvious that their superior speed would carry them clear of the slower, older, British ships. More strikes were flown from *Formidable* and hits on the Italian ships were reported; more cheers, the tension was easing, the 'Eyeties' were running true to form. The aircraft hit and stopped a cruiser, which turned out to be the *Pola*. Darkness came and brought with it a somewhat confused picture, but still the British clung to the Italians' shirt-tails, and in *Caucasian* eyes reached desperately into the night; not looking for Italians now, but to avoid collision with her own ships. Orders came from the *Warspite*, the flagship, and the Fleet manoeuvred and turned with amazing accuracy; more orders, orders, literally, to get out of the way, and *Caucasian* and her consorts moved over to starboard to give the big ships more sea room. Admiral Sir Andrew Cunningham must be on to something; he was clearing for action; in *Caucasian* the excitement mounted, and her company raked the night with eyes which tried in vain to tear aside the shroud of darkness. *Warspite*, *Barham* and *Valiant* swung into line ahead, the traditional broadside order, their huge guns swivelled, and a deathly hush settled upon the night. News came that there were Italian ships up ahead; it was to be a night action.

In *Caucasian* the uncertainty became unbearable; it would not have been so bad if they could have seen what was happening; at any moment the whole world might erupt into a holocaust of thundering guns and screaming shells as ship fought ship in the night. The Captain kept everyone informed as well as he could. Up ahead one of the enemy was damaged and believed stopped; but, with the heroism born of desperation, they might fight back. The remainder of the enemy fleet could not be far away, and they surely could be expected to come to the aid of their stricken compatriot. No one had a very clear picture of exactly what was happening, or what to expect from the enemy. The uncertainty and the dread of the unknown stalked the night like a mocking phantom. Action was ever a chancy business, but a night action was even more chancy; the chance of collision or of underestimating the enemy strength, and the chance that British ships might become the target of British guns. As the ships steamed through the night these were the thoughts of the men who manned them. What of the coming battle? What of tomorrow, if indeed there would be a tomorrow?

Suddenly the quiet of the night was lighted by the stabbing beam of the destroyer *Greyhound's* searchlight, and there in bold relief upon the sea were the Italian cruisers. *Warspite* opened up with a full broadside and the night was suddenly made brighter by the flash of her mighty guns; the luckless *Fiume*, for such she was, reeled with the impact of shells from almost point-blank range. In the resultant explosion a great sheet of flame leapt skyward, and a million pieces of men and metal were blasted into eternity and the night. As though of negative weight her after gun turret, almost in slow motion it seemed, was lifted like a discarded matchbox and fell into the sea; she staggered drunkenly, blazing from stem to stern, a floating torch to illuminate the carnage which followed. *Barham's* guns swung to the destroyer *Alfieri* who was ahead of the line of enemy ships; another mighty flash, another tremendous roar, and she too was blown to eternity. All guns turned to the next in line, the cruiser *Zara*; the night was lit by another flash, the sky rolled with the thunder of guns, and she too was shattered beyond recognition, blazing furiously and wallowing in the trough of battle lost.

There then came a lull in the battle, quietness reigned for a space of time, and only the glare of the blazing ships and the memories of the watchers told where battle once had been. Suddenly there came another frightful explosion as the cruiser *Fiume* blew up and sank. The Professor, like everyone else, subdued and watching the night's work and the carnage wrought, summed up the feelings of everybody: 'Poor bastards,' he murmured, 'Poor fuckin' bastards,' and turned to rest his forehead against the cool metal of the breach of the idle after gun. There but for the grace of God.... The luckless Italians had not stood a cat in hell's chance; such was the price they had paid for their lack of resolution, lack of effective leadership, and lack of experience of battle upon the seas.

Orders came from the flagship to finish off the stricken cruiser and destroyer; *Caucasian* swung to the helm, and with others of her company went in to administer the *coup de grâce*. The long sigh of compressed air which sent the torpedoes upon their errand of final destruction was as if the whole ship's company had sighed with relief; relief that it was all over and that they were still alive to tell the tale. But, though the Italian Fleet would cease to be an effective fighting force hereafter, the *Luftwaffe* still ruled the air; and, as dawn lightened the sky, they were back again. It mattered not that British destroyers were picking up survivors from sunken Italian ships, the dive bombers still came at them and blasted friend and foe alike; and when they ran out of bombs they raked the sea with their machine guns. The British destroyers abandoned their errand of mercy and ran for the east at maximum speed; to the east, but not to the comparative safety of Alexandria harbour; they raced to the succour of a crumbling Greece, and the rescue of a British Army.

Chapter 6

Crete

'Laurels grow in the Bay of Biscay, I hope a bed of them may be found in the Mediterranean.'

Captain Horatio Nelson to the Right Honourable Sir Gilbert Eliot, Bt.
4 August, 1794.

After a few, essential hours in Alexandria, *Caucasian* again headed north, back in action: the scream of dive bombers filled the air and everyone leapt to his post. Bombs whistled down to explode alongside the fast-steaming, keeling destroyer; near miss followed near miss, cascades of water were thrown over the ship, and there came the clang of metal against metal; the Germans were using anti-personnel bombs; another piece of frightfulness to complicate further the lives of simple sailors. The air was filled with deadly pieces of flying metal, metal with jagged and sharpened edges which left furrows and dents in the ship's upper works and could rip the guts out of a man.

Sweating, toiling men glared skywards and cursed. Guns traced through wide arcs and barked defiance at the screaming aircraft, the ship shook to the pounding of her own guns, and she wormed and twisted like a front-row forward as time and time again she responded to helm and missed destruction by feet.

Suddenly on the after pom-pom sponson there was a frightful half-scream, half-shout from the Professor who stood momentarily transfixed with horror; what was left of the 'General's' head flopped grotesquely on to his shoulder and his body slumped lifeless out of the gun layer's chair on to the deck. Hurriedly, and without gentleness, the Professor pulled the 'General' to one side; hurriedly and without gentleness because he could not bear to look at the corpse. With his anti-flash gear splashed bright with the 'General's' blood, he threw himself into the gun layer's chair to keep the gun firing and to try not to think about his dead messmate. But it was not easy to forget your chum lying there, headless and dead. 'Old "Gens" dead – Christ! It could have been me! Poor old "Gens" – Mrs "Gens" can have her fuckin' divorce now all right – and long may she prosper!'

Darkness came and the bombers went away, the sky grew silent, and far off to starboard a beautiful, full cheese of a moon climbed into the cloudless sky and sent long shimmering beams across the empty sea to where *Caucasian* steamed at reduced speed, and only the subdued hum of her engines and the soft intonations of her Captain's voice disturbed the stillness of the night:

'O Eternal Lord God, who alone spreadest out the heavens,
and rulest the raging of the sea.'

With heads bared every man in the ship's company stood silent, numbed, and with tears in their eyes.

'We therefore commit the bodies of these our brethren to the deep.'

The 'General' had not died alone. The shrouding White Ensigns lost their meaningful contours, the side was piped by the Bosun's Party and after a series of subdued splashes the ship's company turned away, and in their hearts there was a great sorrow as they mourned dead shipmates.

After Matapan there was no respite; *Caucasian* and the other destroyers were hard worked and sorely pressed. Malta was revictualled thanks to the destroyers. Rommel's supply lines across the narrows were harassed and his transports sunk, thanks to the destroyers. Tripoli was bombarded by the big ships, escorted by destroyers. The Inshore Squadron landed stores for beleaguered Tobruk, supported by destroyers. The destroyers escorted and raided, nosed and probed, patrolled the Aegean and policed the Dodecanese, and few indeed were the days when they were spared the harrowing assaults of the *Luftwaffe*.

Down through the mountain passes of Greece the Panzer Divisions rolled; through the passes and out onto the plains; through Larissa, Pharsalus, Lamia, Levadia, Thebes, Eleusis, and on to the plain of Athens, until the hills which encompass the shrine of men's aspiration echoed to the thunder of their guns, and men feared for the sanctity of the very hill of the Acropolis itself. Nothing was inviolate before the Nazi onslaught.

As the rape of Greece developed, Piraeus, the port of Athens, became a major objective which had to be taken at all cost, and quickly. Late into the day the battle raged with ships and shore batteries fighting back the screaming bombers and advancing tanks. Men prayed for darkness and the respite it would bring; but there was to be no respite this night; darkness closed in and still the bombers came, guided on to their targets by the light of the fires which raged in the town.

Too valuable to be risked needlessly in the harbour, *Caucasian* and the other warships lay off the entrance and, as the night wore on, the attacks increased in intensity; there were aircraft everywhere, and despite the hazards of night flying and the heavy barrage, they roared in low over the town and spewed death and destruction from their bellies. But the noise of the attacks was as nothing compared with that which followed. Suddenly the entire harbour erupted into a vast, roaring, indescribable holocaust; the explosion shook the harbour and the town and mighty sheets of flame licked skywards and flickered in the heavens to die in great, scintillating aureoles of fire. It rained twisted metal, charred timber, and mangled flesh, and a hundred other ingredients of what once had been a proud ship. The *Clan Frazer* had been loaded to the hatch-coamings with ammunition and high explosives; her company had gallantly fought the fire started when she was hit by a bomb, but to no avail; she went up with a night-shattering roar, took ten other ships with her, destroyed the port and half the town, and left the witnesses of her devastation numbed with shock and horror. *Caucasian*, cruising the outer harbour, rocked to the blast; her company gaped shoreward in utter disbelief, and recoiled from the violence of the night.

Daylight proved the devastation; the harbour was destroyed and so was the town, and a shocked populace piled their dead in the streets. Here the sailors, but a few weeks previously, had found fleeting respite from the rigours of war; now the shocked people searched the debris for their dead and maimed, found cover wherever it was to be found, and waited for the final onslaught.

The days and nights which followed were pure nightmare; round-the-clock bombing kept the ships closed up at action stations without break; men suffered from lack of sleep, and lack of proper food; they were grimy with sweat, smoke and spent cordite; they ate and slept when possible, and relieved themselves where they fought, by the guns, in the magazines and on the bridge. Their main sustenance was provided by cups of tea, good, strong 'action tea' and Woodbines. Never had a smoke tasted so good or meant so much, and the tea was pure nectar, drink for the gods of war.

Came the order from on high to evacuate the troops, and the coast of Greece and the islands of the Dodecanese became a vast setting for a game of hide-and-seek as the destroyers, cruisers and transports got the troops out from anywhere there was a harbour or a place to embark. The ships ran the gauntlet of the dive bombers, and for five days and five nights the battle raged. The destroyers shuttled from shore to transport, and transport to shore, and back again; the poor, bloody soldiery staggered down to the ports and beaches of Nauplion, Kalamata and Monemvasia, and they came out to the waiting destroyers haggard and tired, dirty and bedraggled and with hearts gladdened at sight of the Navy. They knew, they said, that Jack would not let them down; they knew that he would be waiting for them at the end of the long road from the north; and they had come from as far away as the Yugoslavian border, from Edhessa, Salonika and Kastoria.

The blind faith of the soldiery was almost pathetic. They were dragged aboard, often off open beaches, numbed with shock, often wounded, wet to the skin and possessed of little more than they stood up in; and they were to find out what a doubtful sanctuary is a ship in narrow waters. On each trip out to the transports the warships were loaded to the gunwales, the guns blazed defiance at the merciless dive bombers from decks jammed from stem to stern with troops, airmen, civilians and often enough women and children, and it became increasingly difficult to fight ship.

The Grecian shore was dark and hostile, the German guns thundered from the hills, the tanks rolled through the streets of Athens and what was left of Piraeus and paratroopers descended upon the Corinth Canal to cut off yet another line of retreat for harassed troops. At Holomata the men of *Caucasian* supported with her guns the rearguard action fought in the streets of the town by retreating soldiers whom she had come to rescue. One after the other, amidst terrible scenes of suffering amongst the troops tightly packed between their decks, the transports were sunk and the destroyers had to rescue from the sea the soldiers and others whom they had rescued from the shore. Those who survived the stricken ships and the bombs in the sea then fell victim to the dive bombers' machine guns as they were strafed in the water, and in their thousands the dead and mutilated floated lifelessly upon the bloody sea.

Caucasian's upper deck became a casualty clearing station. The Medical Officer and his assistants moved among the stricken men, saved those who could be saved, and did their utmost for those who died; and still the dive bombers came and raked the ships with their cannon, and men who had just been rescued from out the sea jumped back in again, and the number of dead and wounded mounted with every fresh attack. *Caucasian*'s upper deck became untenable, men cowered behind her armoured plates and sheltered from the hail of screaming lead wherever they could find somewhere to crouch, and she numbered among the dead another twelve of her company. The Surgeon Lieutenant was killed on deck in the act of tending the wounded, 'Tug' Wilson was killed on 'A' gun, and 'Stripey' Ackers was blown overboard and never seen again.

The destroyers *Diamond* and *Wryneck* were hit and sunk shortly after picking up survivors from the transport *Slamat*, and one thousand men died. From these three ships only fifty men survived, eight of whom were soldiers, and numbered among them were men who had already survived two transports and one destroyer; and so it went on, the days and nights of hell upon earth followed each other without let up; men dropped at their action stations from sheer exhaustion, and *Caucasian* ran out of ammunition.

Thus the ships, fighting a rearguard action, fell back on Crete, disembarked the soldiery and beat to the south for Alexandria and a few days respite; for the first time in five weeks a whole day passed without the call to action stations and the soul-destroying round of bombs and screaming planes. Men took off their clothes for the first time in three weeks and wallowed in the luxury of a hot shower; they ate four meals a day, and no small number went ashore and got stinking drunk; and still there was no mail from home. Men brooded, and the spirit was all gone out of them; it was only by being driven ruthlessly about the business of ship's husbandry, and ammunitioning and storing ship, that they stayed sane and kept going; but keep going they did, and when the call came for yet another superhuman effort the men of the Mediterranean Fleet rekindled their spirits and rose to the occasion.

Meanwhile news came of the heaviest air raid of the war to date on London; Hitler's reprisal for a British raid on a 'cultural and residential' district of Berlin. Up the coast of North Africa a little way, a bare few hours steaming to the west, the Afrika Korps under General Rommel had pushed the British back on Tobruk. German armies occupied Greece, and the whole basin of the eastern Mediterranean was encircled by a great, hostile pair of pincers, and the only thing which kept the pincers from snapping shut were a handful of hard-run, battle-scarred destroyers. In Alexandria the Royal Navy took stock of its casualties. *Gallant* was gone, so was *Mohawk*, *Diamond* and *Wryneck*, and the transports *Ulster Prince*, *Pennland*, *Slamat*, and *Costa Rica*; all gone, all sunk. *Mohawk* had been chummy ship to *Caucasian*.

The days passed, everyone was thankful for the rest and some of the spirit returned to the ship. Letters were written home without the faintest idea of when, if ever, they would get there; but a man had to cling to something, and letter-writing was a panacea for many ills. One evening the Professor's nose was buried in a book.

'What's the book, Prof?' asked 'Darby' Allen.

'No poxy Orchids for Miss bleedin' Blandish I 'spect!' guffawed 'Scouse' Orrigan from where he sat at the messdeck table staring at a blank sheet of paper and chewing on the end of his pencil. With bright, inquisitive sparrowlike eyes, he had sat thus for over an hour, cudgelling his brains for inspiration to write to his Ma. 'Scouse' was no letter writer, and now he saw his chance to stir things up a bit and thus relieve the tedium of composition.

'Matter of fact,' the Professor answered, 'it is something like that – all about gangsters, rape, arson, pillage, incest, murder, treason and stuff like that.'

'G'wan,' said 'Scouse'; 'Lyin' sod – yew don't read stuff like that!'

'But I do,' corrected the Professor 'but in this case the cops and robbers lived in Florence and Rome about four or five hundred years ago – in Florence, in Rome, in Venice and in what is now Genoa and places like that. It doesn't matter whether it was the battles for the papal succession or the battles of Al Capone in Chicago, they all follow a very similar pattern. There is more action, brutality, and sex, if that's what you look for in a book, in this sort of book than in all your tuppenny bloods put together, and it is a damned sight more interesting because it all happens to be true. Try it sometime and see.'

'P'raps I will,' said 'Scouse': 'I'll 'ave a bash – might improve me mind.' He laughed at what was meant to be a joke at his own expense.

'No good finkin' yew'll improve yore mind, you hignorant Scousewegian bastard!' snorted 'Sludge' Coles contributing his twopennyworth. 'Yew ain't gotta bleedin' mind!'

'That's wher' yew'm wrong, "Sludge" me ol' fruit.' Indignation from 'Scouse'. 'I knows about fings like that – that there Renaysance stuff is a open book ta me. I knows that ol' Caesar Borgia used ta screw 'is sister – yew pass over a book, Prof an' I'll 'ave a bash – teach these bleedin' hignoramusses a fing or three!' Scouse snorted his contempt for the intellectual hoi polloi and retired into a corner with Gilbert Murray on Ancient Greece – a gift, amongst many other books, to the ship's library from Lloyds of London.

So passed the few short days of respite from war, but it was short-lived, and the Fleet put to sea again. The situation had worsened; the island of Crete, the last stronghold, was threatened and once again the Royal Navy raced to the rescue of a British army.

Crete lay dark and vulnerable in the night, a far off pinpoint of light blinked a friendly recognition, and the ships dispersed to their patrol areas; two cruisers and five destroyers to the east of Cape Sidheros, one cruiser and three destroyers to the west of Kithira, more ships to the south of the island, and the battle squadron cruised the area to the east; and so rose the curtain on the Battle of Crete, one of the bloodiest and most costly battles in naval history.

As the thunderheads of war rumbled over Crete another battle was being fought in the west as Force H from Gibraltar pushed through another convoy to Malta; and, still further west, in the mist-shrouded wastes of the North Atlantic, the German battleship *Bismarck* was being hounded to destruction by ships of the Home Fleet from Scapa Flow.

Such was the backdrop to this modern Grecian tragedy.

The days passed, tension mounted, and the first casualty came when the destroyer *Juno* was sunk by dive bombers. The ships patrolled to the north of the island by night and retired to the south by day, and wreaked havoc amongst the German transports of an attempted seaborne invasion. *Caucasian*, with all guns blazing, went into the attack and paid off a few old scores. It was like a shooting gallery, the German troops tightly packed in the transports stood no chance at all; thousands died, blown to pieces at almost point-blank range by the guns, or drowned, weighted down by their equipment.

There came a morning just after dawn when *Caucasian* was pursuing a lone patrol, and there came the sound of heavy aircraft overhead, but there was no attack. The coast of Crete erupted in puffs of smoke and, faintly over the sea, was heard the sound of rising battle. Up into the morning air went the flak, and down came the bombs; more heavy formations overhead and, as *Caucasian* sped to her prearranged rendezvous, the lookouts cried: 'Look, look, paratroopers!'

No formal report and no bearing were given; none was needed; the sky over the island was dotted with the airborne troops swinging lazily and pendulum-like beneath their silvery canopies as they floated earthward. Wave after wave of the airborne troops went into land on the island, and *Caucasian* raced to spread abroad the tidings; here was another departure from the norm of war, another innovation from a superbly equipped German army. On the island the fighting was bitter; outclassed and outfought by a numerically superior and better equipped enemy the British and Commonwealth troops fought their way back to the island's coast, and the Royal Navy could only watch and wait with the catch of the back door lifted in readiness for the exodus which was bound to come.

At dawn the following day to the south of the island of Antikithira *Caucasian* and her consorts met up and, as they took station astern of the cruisers, all hell broke loose. The raiders circled to the east into the rising sun and one after the other peeled off into the attack; toil and sweat, shout and swear, and the dive bombers pulled out of their dives with their rudders almost scraping the mastheads of the ships they attacked. All day long the battle raged, and as soon as one group of bombers had shed their load and gone off to fetch more another group took their place. Darkness brought relief, the bombers returned to base, the guns grew silent and cold and the fresh sea breezes cooled men's bodies and dried the perspiration from their clothes as they savoured the peace of the night.

On the upper deck of *Caucasian*, amid the after-action labours, Jacky Fisher, Leading Torpedoman, was relating how he had received such a fright, owing to the unhealthy proximity of a stick of bombs, that he had messed his trousers, thrown the befouled garments overboard in disgust, and went through the remainder of the action not wearing any trousers or underpants at all!

'Took a bleedin' awful chance there, Jacky boy,' 'Gunga Din' guffawed. 'Yew wus askin' to get yoreself kippered – 'specially wiv all they randy kipper bosuns (Torpedomen) 'anging about!'

'Bloody nigh caught 'is bollocks in the lid of the ammo locker Jacky did!' said 'Sludge' Coles.

'Bloody good job 'e didn't nip 'em orf when the lid slammed down!' 'Sludge' howled. 'Wot a deaf – wot a bleedin' deaf – 'is missus 'ould uv sued the rotten Hadmirality!'

Everybody fell about laughing.

'If 'e 'ad nipped the bastards orf they'd uv prob'ly got shot at they Jerries

– that 'ould 'ave shook the bastards! Fancy gettin' shot down by Jacky's bollocks!'

Everybody had hysterics.

'Oh, Jesus, – packidup!' Johnny Thomas gasped, tears running down his cheeks, ' 'fore I pees me drawers!'

'Fender Belly' Robinson emerged from his magazine like a troglodite from his cavern, and his voice was soon heard booming in his galley as he and the lesser of his ilk prepared a meal; roundly he cursed the Navy, the war, the Germans, the ship, and his long-suffering assistants, and the net result of all this activity was corned beef and hardtack and a brew of scalding tea. Later there would be a tot of neat rum – none of your wishy-washy two-of-water-and-one-of-rum stuff, not at action stations – and then about the business of squaring away decks ready for the dawn.

All the second day the battle raged, *Caucasian* bore a charmed life, and only by some God-sent miracle did she survive and just before nightfall she ran out of ammunition. She was not alone in her plight, others of her company were in like state, or very near it, and a fast run through the night fetched the impotent ships to the ammunition lighters of Alexandria; and every man, from the Captain down, toiled and sweated throughout the heat of the day to replenish the magazines. With the coming of night they put to sea again and ran to the west, the final decision to evacuate had come through and they raced to the rescue.

Everyone dreaded the return to Crete, but there was no time for dread. The recent battles had cost the Navy dear in ships and men; too many ships had met their end in recent weeks; too many ships and too many friends had died there already. Dread was an unaffordable luxury. Ships and friends they once had been; brave men and proud ships; ships with names: *Juno*, *Greyhound*, *Gloucester*, *Fiji*, *Kelly*, *Kashmir* and *Kipling*. All gone, all sunk, and most of their ship's companies with them.

Ashore in Alexandria the Arabs were opening shop and gloating in anticipation of the arrival of the armies of the Third Reich; such pickings there would be! Noses were being thumbed at the retreating British. 'When Germans come' was a favourite expression, and one of the most sought-after things were imitation one pound notes dropped on the surrounding desert by the German Air Force. On the back of these was printed in English and Arabic a promise signed with a facsimile of the signature of Adolf Hitler himself: 'We, the Government of the Third Reich, promise to pay to the bearer the sum of one pound sterling when our victorious armies enter Cairo.'

Back to sea went the Mediterranean Fleet, such as was left, and the evacuation of Crete became a reality. The soldiery fought their way back to the sea; to the north where there were beaches, and to the south where there were ports but no beaches, only precipitous cliffs, the retreating troops gave every inch of ground grudgingly. Footsore and weary, hungry and battle-stained, retreating yes, defeated never, they swarmed aboard *Caucasian* where she lay alongside the wall at Iraklion on the island's northern shore, and the pitiless dive bombers screamed out of the sky and threw everything they had at them; only darkness could help now, and with the darkness the feverish activity of loading the destroyers and ferrying the human cargoes out to waiting cruisers; daylight loading had proved impossible, so the troops sheltered as best they could by day. Each of the waiting ships was to load as many as possible and be well on the way back to Alex before dawn. But such was not to be; with dawn *Imperial* was damaged and had to be sunk by *Hotspur* which loaded the survivors before sinking the stricken ship, and was then herself sunk and a thousand men died. The rising day and the swarming aircraft caught the men who struggled in the water around the stricken ships; they dive-bombed the ships that went to the rescue and when their bombs were spent used their cannon to strafe the mass of men who struggled in the sea. The stoutest hearts wept with horror and grief; laden down with battledress, equipment and boots, the soldiers stood no chance; they died in their thousands.

The ships paid heavily for the delay in getting away, and the day was well advanced before they turned to the south-east and ran for Alexandria. Ships which had turned back to the aid of the men who had struggled in the water found no similar humanity at the hands of the *Luftwaffe*, and the dive bombers chased them to the limit of effective aircraft range.

Discounting her dead and wounded, *Caucasian* boasted one hundred and ninety men in her ship's company; she now carried an additional eight hundred troops – a thousand men crammed her decks. The guns blazed; the bombs exploded with a roar and a deluge of water which soaked the soldiery to the skin; shrapnel exacted a terrible toll. Wishing they were anywhere but in a ship the troops could do nothing but pray and cower around the superstructure. Flak streamed skyward, but nothing could stop the maniacs of the *Fliegerkorps*; their cannon wreaked havoc on the decks of the ship, and men slumped dead in their comrades' arms because there was not enough room to fall down.

'You dirty murdering bastards!' the Professor screamed into the battle-riven sky, glared through his gunsight with murder in his heart, and squeezed the firing mechanism until his hands were sore. He swung the belching pom-poms yet again, the enemy cannon shells spattered into the gun shield and ricocheted off into the mass of troops cowering about the deck; then, almost without realizing it, he saw the shells from his piston-actioned barrels ripping into the black underbelly of a screaming Ju 88. Just before it hit the water, it blew up with a shattering roar and a force which sent the ship reeling. A ragged cheer was raised, and over the intercom came the voice of the Captain: 'Well done, Martin-Smith; we'll have a swastika on the funnel for that!'

With a feeling of satisfaction the Professor eased back in his chair; that evened the score a bit.

'Nice shooting, Prof!' shouted Johnny Thomas, number two of the gun since the death of the 'General' and the promotion of the Professor. The thumbs up sign came from all over the ship.

Once again shells from the pom-poms ripped into the belly of a diving Ju 88, but no one saw what happened to that one; it must have dropped its bombs at the moment of being hit and *Caucasian* was suddenly devastated by a terrific explosion. With a deafening, mind-engulfing, eyeball-searing, body-shattering roar the whole forepart of the ship was blasted to kingdom come; twisted metal, woodwork and bits of bodies were blown high into the air and rained down upon the indifferent sea. At the moment of impact she was doing thirty-six knots and simply ploughed herself under; in an instant she was gone, and only the debris and body-littered sea told of her going.

The Professor would always remember, in this instant of fleeting, memory-imprinting catastrophe, seeing a man, a whole uniformed, living man, blasted bodily against the funnel, there to hang spread-eagled, arms and legs flung wide and a silly grin on his face; he recognized Darby Allen, the silly grin faded, and Darby just disintegrated.

When the Professor regained consciousness he was surfacing in the debris-strewn sea, *Caucasian* was nowhere to be seen and there came from the sea a belch of released air from the sunken ship which briefly disturbed the water. At this moment a feeling of thankfulness overwhelmed him, a great elation; he had survived; he was alive! He gasped and gulped air into his lungs and, for no apparent reason, struck out; to where he proposed to swim he knew not and cared less, he just had to prove by violent physical exertion that he was indeed still alive. Reaction then came and he trod water, his lungs rasped from salt water and deep immersion, and he vomited into the sea. Looking about he could see wreckage everywhere and, here and there, heads bobbing in the water. Men called to each other and pushed aside the corpses as they swam to unite with the living. Together they clung to pieces of wreckage and to each other whilst in the near distance a destroyer, continuously sounding off with her siren, raced to the scene to pick up survivors; despite the ferocious attacks of the dive bombers, she went about the business of rescue. Quickly the few, pitifully few, survivors were all aboard and, bearing a charmed life, guns blazing and engines throbbing, she came about in a wide arc and raced for Alexandria and comparative safety; despite all that the dive bombers threw at her, she made it.

Dazed, numbed with shock and grief, the Professor wandered around for days like a man without a soul. His ship was gone, and with her had gone his friends, and with them had gone some eight hundred soldiers whom he and his shipmates had rescued from the shores of Crete. When the count was made, and the pieces all fitted together, it was found that twenty-three men had survived *Caucasian* – twenty-three very lucky men. Of the Professor's intimates only Johnny Thomas and 'Dodger' Long had survived, and only one officer, 'Paddy' Flynn, the Warrant Gunner (T) (Torpedoes). All the rest, from the Captain down, had perished. It was too terrible to contemplate; the magnitude, the personal calamity of the loss made his senses recoil in horror from the memory. Johnny Thomas had survived because he had been shielded by the same gun shield which had saved the Professor's life; he, too, had been blown overboard. How 'Dodger' had got away even he had no idea; he had been in the forward magazine and all that he could remember was a tremendous bang and waking up in the water. It was nothing short of a miracle; that magazine had been right in the heart of the ship for'ard of the bridge and right where the bomb had exploded. 'Dodger's' mind was affected, not seriously, but enough to put him in hospital for a considerable spell.

It was a very reduced Fleet that reassembled in Alexandria harbour; the losses in ships and men had been frightful. *Hotspur*, *Imperial*, *Hereward*, *Calcutta*, *Coventry* and *Caucasian* sunk; *Orion, Dido* and *Perth* badly damaged and, from the opening of the Battles of Greece and Crete, these were but a few of the total losses.

Badly mauled, but with its spirit far from broken, the Fleet lay at Alexandria, licked its wounds, and prepared for the next round – the battle for the Middle East had only just begun.

The rescued army had disembarked and gone its way on the long, hard road to El Alamein, and the survivors from the ships were sent to the naval base and transit camp at Sidi Birsh (Bish) on the outskirts of Alexandria, there to await Their Lordships' pleasure; in many cases a return to the ships of the Fleet in the Middle East and a return to the battleground, and in others to form up the crews which would steam the damaged ships to repair yards outside the immediate theatre of war.

HMS *Sphinx*, the naval base, existed to maintain the two-way traffic between the Mediterranean Fleet and the United Kingdom; between ships which wanted men, and men who did not particularly want ships. Here the survivors from *Caucasian* were issued with new kit and generally assisted back to sanity; in the days of readjustment that followed, the Professor looked back upon the terrible days in Greece and Crete and upon the tragic end of his ship, and there was a deep and abiding sorrow in his heart. She had had her share of skates (men always in trouble), pompey dodgers (workshy) and rogues, but she had been as good as any other ship and better than most.

The Professor would not, could not, ever forget *Caucasian*. He remembered old 'Pappy' Pringle's off-key tenor voice in the bathroom, 'Fender Belly's' booming laugh, 'Postey' Richardson's six kids back in Devonport, six kids upon whom he doted; the Chief Yeoman with his rheumy eyes and snotty nose, 'Yanto's' promiscuity, 'Stripey' Ackers at the rum fanny, and the funereal Ivor ('Doc') Payne the Sick Berth Tiffy who read the Bible every night before he turned in; the prinking, the preening, and the titivating, as they all prepared to step ashore; and the bedraggled, bleary-eyed, stagger back on board again.

Johnny Thomas snapped his fingers under the Professor's nose, and his friend came back to earth with a start.

'Hey, c'mon! – get with it – we goin'?'

'Eh, yeah, – of course.' The Professor stretched. 'Feel like goin' ashore an' gettin' pissed!'

'Me, too.' Thomas reached for his shorts. 'Let's go an' get stinkin' drunk!'

The pair dressed and walked to the main gate; there they insulted the Arab peanut vendor who had been taught by legions of sailors to swear most atrociously in English as he hawked his wares. 'Up your fat ass, 'Hooky'!' he greeted them and, after teaching him a few words to add to his vocabulary, they bought a bag of peanuts, caught the tram to Alexandria and got stoned out of their minds.

Chapter 7

Transatlantic Interlude

'A few months' rest I must have, very soon. If I am in my grave, what are the mines of Peru to me?'
Vice Admiral Lord Nelson to Lady Hamilton. 23 November, 1804.

HMS *Sphinx* was overrun with survivors from sunk or damaged ships and the camp's resources were strained to the limit; but, despite the cramped conditions and the inconveniences, it was paradise compared with the experience of recent months.

Johnny Thomas and the Professor had been in camp for forty-eight hours and were enjoying the rest and suffering the hangover, but they were not to be left in peace for long. The struggle for supremacy in the Middle East continued unabated; casualties had to be replaced and ships kept manned. Every hour men were leaving to take the place of others who had been killed in action or maimed in the ships which harassed Rommel's supply lines, ran the gauntlet to Malta, bombarded the coast or patrolled the Central Basin from Haifa in the east to Malta in the west, and from the coast of Greece in the north to Alexandria in the south. Ceaselessly, relentlessly, the hard-pressed, overworked, and battle-weary ships went about the affairs of war. The fact that a man had just survived one ship, or two or three, in no way made him ineligible to serve in another, and the base was inundated with calls from harassed Captains. Drafting office windows were no place for wit and banter those days.

The crystal ball having been duly consulted, the Drafting Regulating Petty Officer poked his head out of the window and in a bad-tempered voice read out a list of names. His words were met with stony silence; not a man there was in the least bit eager to face the dive bombers again or to march up to General Rommel's front lines with any one of the numerous naval parties which were being formed up to assist the army because there were not enough ships to go around.

'Able Seaman Rogers, J.B.!' barked the RPO.

'Aye, aye!' came the seaman-like response.

'HMS *Phoebe*– gityerbaganhammickpackedandgitbackyersharpish!'

'Leading Stoker Murphy, P.J. – bet yore bleedin' name's Pat – HMS *Warspite*– gityerbaganhammick.'

'Stores Assistant Perkins, G.R. – 'Polly', you'm goin' ta St Angelo'. The RPO positively gloated. 'Malta – you'm goin' through by submarine – gityerbaganhammick.'

So the list was whittled down; men came and went, often without time to unpack a kitbag – if they were lucky enough to have one.

'Able Seaman – Christ! what an' 'andle – wotsit? – Walter Pater Martin bleedin' hayfen Smiff – where did they dig yew outa; the bleedin' Ritz? HMS *Orient*.'

At the wit of the exalted and those placed in authority above poor luckless matelots the Professor permitted himself a wry smile.

'Able Seaman Thomas, J. – yew too – *Orient*– gityerbaganhammick – back yer by fourteen hundred – you'm both goin' this atternoon.'

'Well thank goodness we both got the same ship – an' without working a fiddle.'

'Cruisers are a bit different from destroyers though,' replied the Professor. 'Big ship sailors eh – bit of a come down after destroyers.'

'Not too bloody far down I 'ope,' Thomas replied with a bit of a funny laugh. 'Did 'ear as 'ow she is in a bit uv a state – last time we saw 'er she was taking a right pastin' wiv the ol' *Dido* up off Crete – did 'ear as 'ow she's got nearly five 'undred dead in 'er, mostly all Pongoes (soldiers).'

Arrival at the coaling jetty in Alexandria harbour proved *Orient* to be in a bad state indeed. Acetylene torches spluttered in the hot afternoon sun, cranes were pulling great chunks of twisted metal out of her, and everywhere was bustle and activity as men went about the business of clearing away and patching the great battle scars in her superstructure and broadside compartments. Her upper deck abaft the single funnel was a shambles, her hull abaft midships was badly damaged, luckily above the water line, and everywhere she was covered with the grime and filth of battle. It would be a long time before *Orient* was fit to fight again. Ominous blanket-covered figures on stretchers were still being carried from out of the wreckage, and sailors removed their caps and averted their gaze when the dead passed by. Five hundred dead had been no exaggeration; there were four hundred and eighty and an even larger number of wounded.

As the new arrivals settled into the for'ard messdecks the winds of rumour fanned the embers of men's hopes. *Orient* was going for docking, she was going to South Africa, to Singapore and to a dozen other places conjured from out the wishful thinking of battle-weary men. Bookmakers thrived; Singapore ran favourite with Durban, Hong Kong and Trincomalee heading the rest of the betting at short odds; and, on the day of the final call over, the day the ship sailed, Blighty was quoted at evens.

With the coming of night *Orient* was gone and in the days that followed everyone worked hard; patches here, canvas screens there, and to make the ship seaworthy and to embalm the dead who were already stinking to high heaven, concrete was poured into the inaccessible places. An atmosphere of shock still pervaded the ship.

Starboard wheel to Port Said, the canal, Suez and the Red Sea. The dome of the Custom's House and the outlines of the offices of the Suez Canal Company were discernible to starboard as *Orient* slipped into the canal. The ship's company started to relax; every turn of the screws put them that much further away from the Mediterranean. The Bitter Lakes and the Anzac Memorial gave way to Port Tewfik and the causeway to Port Suez and, as dawn was breaking over the canal, the sight of a British troopship lazily puffing smoke into a peerless sky brought a cheer from the men who lined the rails of both ships. The soldiers were singing as they disembarked, and the sight of the badly damaged cruiser brought the proceedings to a silent, temporary standstill as *Orient* slipped past. The soldiers, desert bound, saw the shape of things to come; Jack was going he knew not where. 'Good ol' Tommy!' 'Best uv luck, Jack!' And *Orient* limped to the south and east.

Arab dhows, huge of sail and heavily burdened with strange cargoes, came in close, their crews consumed with curiosity at sight of the cruiser's gaping battle scars. The boatmen jabbered excitedly amongst themselves, pointed to the roughly patched holes, and passed astern with hands cupped to mouths and long drawn out wails of 'Waaa-hyaaah'.

'Porky' Pine, one of *Orient*'s original ship's company, and a three-badge Stoker, spat over the side from where he was holding court on the starboard for'ard fairlead. To say that he sat on the fairlead puts rather too fine a point on it: he enveloped it. 'Porky' was well endowed and to the assembled company taking an after breakfast smoke, he said: 'I've 'eard some bloody funny tales about them Ayrabs; they do say as 'ow they still do's a bit uv slave tradin' round these parts – an' they certainly trades in " 'ubbly-bubbly" (hashish). This is the ol' narcotics road uv the east.'

'Proper rum country if yew asks me,' 'Speaky' Lowe, Ordinary Seaman, chipped in his twopennyworth. 'What do they do wiv them slaves when they got 'em then "Porks"?'

Porky, like so many old three badgers, was a veritable storehouse of tall stories, travel lore, strange tales, and lower deck philosophy; he settled his fat backside more firmly astraddle the fairlead and slowly, and with irritating deliberation, rolled himself a tickler (home-made cigarette). He then looked around to gauge the interest being shown by his audience, mostly young ABs or equivalent and, satisfied that they were hanging on his every word, continued: 'Do wiv 'em, wadya fink they do's wiv 'em – they sells the bastards uv course – sells 'em to wealfy sheiks an' gyppoes – an' to broffels uv course, – that's if they'm wimmin.'

'If they'm wimmin?'

'Yeah, if they'm wimmin.' 'Porky' savoured the moment he struck oil, and dwelt a pause whilst he waited for the inevitable question.

'What if they ain't wimmin?' asked 'Speaky'.

'They still sells 'em – that's if they'm young enuff an' 'andsum wiv it.'

'Porky' was being deliberately tantalizing. ' 'Ave yew 'eard tell as 'ow they uses ewnucks in these parts?'

'Wot's a ewnuck, "Porks"?'

'Ain't yew bastards never 'eard uv a ewnuck? – they'm queer fellas – brown 'atters – 'at-racks – yew know – 'omosexuals – but 'omosexuals wot ain't 'omosexuals if yew takes my meaning.'

They did not, but it was 'Porky's' intention that not for long would they remain in a state of ignorance about such matters. 'They'm deliberately made into queers when they'm young.' 'Porky' relished the telling. 'They Ayrabs cuts off their cocks an' their balls and makes it so that they ain't got no sexual ambitions no more – then they screws 'em summat rotten!'

His audience shuddered.

'Garn!' Disbelief from 'Speaky'.

' 'Strewf!' affirmed 'Porky', 'It's all part uv their religion – ol' Mahomet said that man wot gets born outa man shall live forever an' be 'eralded as the son of the prophet or summat – sez so in the Koran – 'member ol' Lawrence uv Arabia in that book uv 'is called *Seven Pillars of Wisdom*? – 'e 'ad to get screwed by 'em 'relse they'd uv rumbled that 'e weren't really no Ayrab.'

Heads nodded; the mention of *Seven Pillars of Wisdom* gave the story a touch of authenticity. 'Porky' went on to describe in graphic detail how boys are taken from the villages and seaports of Africa's east coast, from Port Sudan to Zanzibar, before they reach the age of puberty; their sexual organs are then removed with a knife; a wooden peg soaked in hot pitch is then inserted into the wound and, after recovering from this atrocity, they are sold to the highest bidder and, deprived of the potential for manhood, enter the household of the buyer where they are groomed as concubines and used like the women with whom they are brought up; always with the end in view that one day one of these unfortunate creatures will conceive and give birth, and the wealthy owner will achieve immortality as the father of the Promised of Allah.

'Porky's' audience digested the facts.

'Come to fink about it, there must be sumthin' in it,' Johnny Thomas hugged his knees where he sat 'Go-West-Young-Man' fashion on the deck. ' 'Relse there'd be no point in 'avin' ewnucks.'

'Thought,' the Professor chipped in, 'that they were trimmed and trained as harem keepers just so that they could not entertain lecherous designs on the sheik's wives.'

'That,' Porky replied, 'is where yew'm wrong – that's only part uv their job – they only does that when they gets too old fer screwin'.'

'Cor, an' to fink I always fancied a job in a 'arem – no fank yew very much – not at that price – I likes me oats too much fer that!' 'Lanky' Rowbottom shuddered. 'Wotta bleedin' life!'

This caused a laugh and the usual repartee. Johnny Thomas then related the story of the Arab gentleman's reason for always wearing baggy trousers tied at the bottoms – to catch the baby if they gave birth.

Amidst howls of laughter 'Porky' tucked the bottoms of his overall trousers into his socks, hitched his overalls more tightly around his pendulous belly and, holding aloft his arms, did an elephantine pirouette. 'Can't be too bleedin' careful!' he said chortling.

That folded them up, and when someone presented 'Porky' with a pair of bicycle clips, conjured from who knew where, they fell about. The old spirit was returning to the sailors of *Orient*; life was coming back to the ship.

On the run down to Aden 'Red Sea Routine' was instigated; a routine whereby the hands were turned to at 0530 and secured for the day at 1100, the remainder of the day being free time. The ship had been cleaned as much as possible, but there were still hundreds of dead bodies down below embalmed in concrete and everyone avoided these areas. There was not a lot of work left to be done, so relaxation was the rule; a wise Captain had decreed it be so and rumour had it that the ship was bound for the United States of America. It was generally assumed that she would round the Cape of Good Hope and cross the South Atlantic on a nor'west heading; a book, in fact a number of books, was made on her destination. New York was favourite, until it was remembered that there were German surface raiders in the South Atlantic and *Orient* was in no fit state to cope with that sort of thing; so the books were rethought, and east about to San Francisco headed the betting list.

After brief calls *en route* at Aden and Trincomalee *Orient* nosed alongside the dockyard wall in Singapore, and every man Jack in her ship's company was on deck for arrival. Naval Law decrees that every man not in the Rig of the Day shall clear off the upper deck when a ship enters harbours; so, this day, to get their first view of this land of Far Eastern promise, the entire ship's company changed into Rig of the Day and every vantage point was manned by erect, motionless, eyeballing matelots anticipating a run ashore and raring to be up and at it; the first real run ashore, 'Yew can't call Aden a real run ashore,' since Alexandria.

The old hands were painting pictures of Singapore which glowed with highlights, halflights, lowlights – very lowlights – and no lights at all; lurid tales of 'I remember', of the amenities offered and the sights to be seen. Nights in the Fleet Canteen; nights of ribald song and libation; of the area around Lavender Street; of rickshaws; the 'New World', the 'Great World', and the 'Happy World'; that is, fairgrounds cum bazaars cum pleasure gardens cum any form of diversion the heart of man can desire, with their dance halls and delightful Malayan, Chinese-Malayan, and Indo-Malayan hostesses; restaurants too numerous to tell of where were available all the gastronomic delights of the east; from chow mein, chop suey, and curries by the score, to Jack's favourite steak, egg and chips. Bars there were also, bars by the thousand; bars with service associations like the White Ensign, or famous bars like the Yen Pin or the bar of the Raffles Hotel: 'Hawkers, circulars and sailors not allowed and keep off the grass whilst you're at it.'

Singapore had beckoned as a beacon beckons the distressed mariner; now here was Singapore. 'Who's fer the beach? Steppin' off, Prof?' 'C'mon, 'Knocker', yew'll do, yew'm proper 'andsome!' Jack titivated and spruced himself up, dressed in his best suit of whites, tried this collar and that, tied a tiddly bow here and a tiddly bow there; cap at the right angle – always give it a bit more list to port once the gangway was cleared. Seven box creases in the trousers, perhaps an extra penny in the bottom seams to give them that little extra swing. 'Wot wus that pipe?' 'Libertymen – Yahoo!' ' 'Ere we go! – 'ang on! – check, check, check, – spectacles, testicles, wallet, and watch – 'andkerchiff, fags, matches, loose change, paybook, and dreadnoughts (condoms) – yew never knows yer luck!'

With grinning rickshaw boys as guides and mentors Jack fanned out to the four corners of the city in pursuit of pleasure. 'Chop, chop, Johnny, we 'aven't got all night – an' we 'aven't 'ad a good run ashore in months. Chop, chop, Johnny! – Imshi! Yalla! Caramba! Allez-vous! Go! Bint! Mademoiselle! Signorina! Girl!' Language was no barrier, Jack speaks them all; so too did the rickshaw boys; they grinned the wider and trotted off with their loads of pleasure-bent matelots, and made straight for where they knew their passengers wanted to go.

Singapore in the summer of 1941 was still a land of peace and plenty, its teeming multitude went about its affairs scarcely disturbed by the tides of war which ebbed and flowed half a world away. Away to the north east, far away, the rays of the Rising Sun cast long shadows, but shed little light here in this rabbit warren of the Johore Straits. Over all fluttered the Union Flag and the White Ensign; people felt safe in their island fortress, safe and far removed from the war from which poor old Jack had just escaped, and that poor ship such a mess too. 'Cheers, Jack, have another – we colonials are nothing if not hospitable – one for the road, old boy, or should it be the sea? Ha, ha, ha, – oh, and bye the bye, don't forget to keep off the grass, old thing!' Dogs and sailors kept off the grass, and out in the Roads the cruisers and destroyers of the Eastern Fleet swung to their anchors and all was well with the colonial world.

The men of *Orient* sampled the delights to the full, and John Thomas and his friend the Professor, ably supported by one 'Buster' Brown, were no laggards in pursuit of pleasure. The beer and the spirits relaxed the tensions of the past year – was it that long? – and they were having a ball at a table in the corner of some anonymous bar cum cabaret in company with three delightful and very attractive Malay girls, and they laughed and they sang as they had not done in a long time.

'That was a cute little rhyme; sing us another one just like the other one, sing us another one do... There was a young lady from Hitchen who was scratching her fanny in the kitchen; her mother said, "Rose, crabs I suppose," and Rose said "Bollocks! Get on with your knitting!" ' Roars of approval, and looks of utter bewilderment from the hostesses. Rhyme followed rhyme, song followed song, drink followed drink and everyone, except the hostesses, got drunk.

'Buster' Brown set the pattern for their future pleasure by becoming engaged in an amorous entanglement with his girlfriend of the evening; she returned his every kiss, and his every intimate caress. Had the party any chaste resolve, being privy to this amorous interplay would have tried such resolve to the utmost; but such resolve they had not, and it was agreed that the party should retire to a place wot of by the ladies, and at a house somewhere in the teeming alleyways of the town the rickshaws were paid off. The house, typical of southern Malaya, possessed rooms by the score; small rooms with bare boards and rush mats, bamboo furniture and monsoon shutters which were closed against the night and the mosquitoes. The party dispersed about the house and the Professor found himself alone with his friendly hostess. He sat upon the bed and gazed at her owlishly, she smiled into his eyes and knelt before him and removed his shoes and, as she offered no resistance, he clumsily undressed her. As the flames of long frustrated passion rose hungrily and consumed any resistance or disinclination he might have felt, his owlishness vanished, as she, naked and with dark-skinned, oriental beauty, offered herself to him; she suffered gladly his embrace and brought into play the ageless, practised, love-making artistry of the east. Through the engulfing suffusion of alcohol and passion there came back the memory of the last time he had lain with a woman; it had been eighteen months ago – so long? And, like him, she had been a student and they had both professed to being free thinkers, free lovers and iconoclasts of convention. Wonder where she is now, he thought. And there in a bamboo room somewhere in the depths of Singapore he surrendered to eastern artistry and made lust as it had never been made before.

With half an hour to get back onboard and the account with the smiling hostesses settled to everyone's satisfaction, the three wended their way towards the dockyard, physically satiated, subdued and possessed of a desire for silence.

The silence was broken by the Professor: 'Fag?'

'Good run ashore.' The Professor spoke to the tops of the dockyard cranes.

'Yeah.' Mutual grunts from the others.

'Didn't spend much.' John Thomas addressed the bows of a parked destroyer.

'No.' From the other two.

'Not bad parties (girls), them.' Buster sought confirmation.

'Not bad.'

'Cheap at ten bob.' Thomas opined.

'Yeah,' the others affirmed, 'Dirt cheap.'

'Better come down the sick bay,' invited 'Buster', ' 'ave a rub at the ol' boogie can (prophylactic appliance) – better be safe than sorry.' With 'Buster' acting in his official capacity as sick berth attendant, the treatment was soon concluded.

The morning after, her ship's company suffering monumental hangovers, *Orient* sailed: south-east for the Karimata Strait, the Java Sea and the broad Pacific.

Through the Karimata Strait and north-east about Cape Selatan on Borneo's south-eastern tip, the Macassar Strait and the Celebes Sea, and on through the narrows between Sarangani and Kepulanan, to set a course east by north-east for the Hawaiian Islands and Honolulu. Glorious sunny days, lazy days and warm romantic nights; but, as 'Buster' said, 'There ain't no bastard to be romantic wiv! Wish we 'ad them parties from Singapore along.' Tropical islands with waving palms and golden sands, any one of which would have done Robinson Crusoe proud; islands set like shining gems in the vast sub-Asian necklace, demi-paradises by their very remoteness. The war was a million miles away. Talaud Island, Palau Islands, Yap, Guam and the Marianas.

In the ship's wake and about her hull were sharks and shark shooting became a popular sport and good small-arms training; until, that is, someone shot the Chief of all the Engine Room Artificers through the starboard lug-'ole – no more shark shooting.

During the two weeks' steaming to Honolulu the main preoccupation was keeping boredom at bay. Every artifice was employed, from 'Uckers' (Ludo on a giant board) and cribbage tournaments to spelling bees and hosepipe battles.

Honolulu had disappointed; the stay was brief. The American overcommercialization of the islands was bizarre and garish; it clashed with all the preconceived notions derived from the products of Hollywood's celluloid forcing houses. Pearl Harbor sheltered the ships of the American

Pacific Fleet, and the city had been overrun with their companies who had proved highly critical of the way 'yew god-damned Limeys are runnin' thet liddle ol' shootin' match back there.' Fights had been inevitable.

Orient pressed ever eastward until one day there came the traditional cry: a cry heard upon these waters for centuries; 'Land ahoy!' was called for the sheer hell of it; and land it was, the coast of the United States of America. Word spread throughout the ship and men came on deck to gape and speculate, and experts there were aplenty; the distance judgers, the 'navigators' from the boiler room, the landfall bookmakers from the Captain's pantry and the judgers of ETA (Estimated Time of Arrival) from the 'Bootnecks' (Royal Marines) Mess. The landfall of Christopher Columbus could hardly have been greeted with greater enthusiasm, and the impression was gained that *Orient*'s ship's company had just discovered America.

From a smudge grew a line, from a line a landmass, and from the blue haze of heat grew a city. Past the prison island of Alcatraz and there was the Golden Gate Bridge towering overhead, its girderwork casting a shadow upon the ship as she passed beneath and its structure forming a frame for the picture of HMS *Orient* entering San Francisco Harbour.

It was a stupendous moment for those aboard; here at last was the land of promise, the land of true peace, God's own country, the culmination of weeks of waiting. Here was peace and plenty after long weary months of war, strain and deprivation; and, as the ship went to her berth in gathering darkness, the Band of the Royal Marines played 'Hearts of Oak' and 'Land of Hope and Glory'. 'Good ol' "Boots" – give it some stick – show the bastards how it's done!'

Lights blazed from the city in their millions; lights which lit the way, lights which flashed on and off in advertisement and the headlights of cars which swept the bay from Columbus Heights and Spy Glass Hill. Here was the land of Hollywood and Los Angeles, Chicago and New York; here were cowboys and Indians, gold rushes and gangsters, prohibition and booze unlimited, millionaires and hoboes who rode the trains, mountains and deserts, mighty trains and fast cars and aeroplanes, honky-tonk and speakeasy, and the White House; Jack Dempsey, Joe Louis, Abraham Lincoln, George Washington, Al Capone and 'Baby-face' Nelson. Here was larger than life, here was all life; here indeed was everything upon which a generation of Britishers had been nurtured and fed from celluloid spoons.

The ship berthed in the Navy Yard and a horde of officials descended upon her; everything was offered; invitations to dinners, dances, receptions and a dockyard refit, and all gratefully accepted; Friends of Britain Societies, Scotsmen in America, Veterans' Associations, the United Services Organization, the League of Navy Wives and a dozen such bodies vied with each other in hospitality. Here was welcome indeed: America opened its heart and its doors to the British ship, and here no one criticized Britain's conduct of the war; the bands played 'See the Conquering Heroes Come' and the heroes of the North Atlantic, Malta, Greece, Crete, Matapan and a dozen other battles conquered in no mean measure. No one from the ship bought his own liquor or slept in his own bed, if indeed he slept at all, and the pace was killing; in fact, if all the stories were to be believed, Jack slept with half the female population of the Pacific coast. An incorrigible 'sleeper with' was Jack, and a great teller of stories, too; and why not? Anything for a laugh; anything for a bloody good run ashore.

Hectic night followed hectic day, the tempo of living rose to such a pitch that it became hard to sustain; Jack slept, if he could, in any odd corner by day, and painted the town, or anywhere else which needed a coat of paint, by night. The ship's telephones rang incessantly as the demand for Jack's services increased, and cars queued at the dockyard gates ready to whisk him away to yet another party, another session with the lads, and everyone had 'up homers' (somewhere to live ashore with a family).

A note of solemnity was introduced when the dead were removed from the ship, still in their concrete funeral shrouds, and buried ashore. The entire ship's company attended the funeral, and the dead of Crete were buried with full Naval Honours in the welcoming bosom of the land their forefathers pioneered. As the volleys rang out over the heights men's thoughts travelled back in time across the thousands of miles of ocean to the war-ravaged Mediterranean; back to lands and a sea which now seemed so very remote, so remote that even the bad dreams no longer disturbed the nights. Jack remembered his friends and shipmates as he stood, with tears in his eyes and head bared to the warm Pacific breeze, and came away saddened from the ceremony of remembering.

Orient's repairs proceeded apace and it became necessary to accommodate some of her company ashore; in the resultant reshuffle some of them were sent east to New York and to Norfolk, Virginia, there to join old friends of the Mediterranean Fleet who were also undergoing repairs in the States; old friends like *Illustrious*, *Formidable* and *Warspite*; friends of doughty deed and imperishable memory. The ships under repair were stripped of some of their companies who were sent to steam home other ships whose repairs had been completed. Men were as valuable as ships because, believe it or not, 'we still gotta war on our 'ands, Jack me ol' fruit.' Draft chits flew like leaves before the autumnal winds and, with fond memories of Saint Francis of the Pacific coast, the Professor and John Thomas found themselves aboard the Pacific Coast Special, a great silver monster of a transcontinental express train, bound for the city of New York, accompanied by some two dozen other ratings and an officer.

To roar through the day and through the night, and all through the next day, proved a great novelty, a never-to-be-forgotten experience; from west coast to east coast of the great north American continent, to sleep in sleeping cars and to take meals in the diner where they acquired a negro attendant to cater for their very modest needs. They acquired the friendly negro attendant because they were friendly toward him and, consequently, he could not do enough for them, the first British sailors he had ever seen. He loved to talk to them about the war, and marvelled at the telling. 'Wal, man alive, waddya all know abaat thet – ain't thet sumfin yews all a tellin' – ain't thet reeaalay sumfin?' And the bombs rained down and ships were sunk all over the salt flats of Utah. His great eyes shone white from the blackness of his features, and his lower lip sagged as he listened, and he too talked of his wife and family back in 'Frisco, of his life on the trains, and of how he hoped, 'Wees'll all 'elp yo out wid dat der war o' yourn, – seems a consid'rable shame man dat all dem mightee fine ships done got rid off an' got demselfs sunk dattaway – pow'ful shame.' He pronounced a liking for British cigarettes, took the merest sip of the whisky he procured on the sailors' behalf, and did many a little service at their behest. Under his ministrations their shoes gleamed with a shining blackness, there was an extra pillow for the berth if needed and a bottom berth where possible.

It came as a shock to come face to face with the colour bar, and the displeasure of a fellow traveller in the form of a big, florid man who, despite the fact that he was eating breakfast, was wearing an outsize hat, the hallmark of a Texan. He approached the table where the sailors sat and the clatter of forks on plates and the hum of conversation died away as he opened with a most profound observation: 'Yew guys are Limeys, ain'cha?'

The Professor put down his knife and fork, looked at the oversized intruder and affirmed that he and his fellows were indeed of that ilk.

'Henry Dodge – Henry K. Dodge from Dallas, Texas,' he boomed with emphasis on the Texas, and on the 'K' in repeating his name; then he grunted 'Cattle', almost as if cattle were of no importance, 'But don't yew guys fergit cattle!'

'Howdyalikamerica?' he asked politely.

'Oh fine,' replied the Professor, 'Just fine.' But he could sense that there was more to this than mere pleasantry. He could sense the threat.

'Shure son, shure – she's mightee fine, mightee fine – an' we aims ta keep 'er thetaway!' Henry K. Dodge, Esquire, was talking to the diner at large. 'But we ain't gonna hev 'er thetaway fer long ef'n yew guys goes around a fussin' up them niggahs!'

His voice carried from one end of the Pullman car to the other, but he was still very polite, deadly polite, and he paused to gauge the effect of his words: 'We gotta live with these uppity black fellas – an' they gits uppitier an' uppitier – yes sir – they's prittee uppity these days – an' the moah yew fusses 'em up the moah uppity they gits, 'til it gits ta be just plain liddle ol' hell – fer them – so ah'm givin' yew all jest a liddle ol' piece o' real friendly advice, boys, which yew'll all take eff'n yew wanna go right on enjoyin' yoah liddle ol' veesit heah – doan't fuss up the black fellas, boys – jest doan fuss 'em up!'

His big hands rested on the table, he leaned his weight on them against the gentle swaying of the coach, and looked hard and long from eye to eye around the table of embarrassed faces. This was something new in the sailors' experience; they looked away. This was deep-down racial hatred. The big Texan, for all his politeness, was potent with menace; the sailors felt the threat, and sensed all the unspoken things, and gazed out upon the mountains of Nevada in silence.

But the Texan was not finished with them yet, and a mighty grin split his face. 'Aah see yew all take ma meaning', boys,' he boomed yet again. 'Now whadda ya hev ta drink? – whusky? – why shure boys – a raaght manlee drink!'

He turned to where the Negro attendant stood wide-eyed and intently watching the scene at the table. 'Whusky, boy; whusky foah ma friends!'

Whisky for breakfast? Why not? And whisky it was, by the bottle, followed by further bottles from embarrassed fellow travellers, and in the dining car all was animated zesty life again. Talk bubbled over and spilled to where the sailors sat, and they were dragged without reluctance into the talk; and there was talk of war, of ships of war, of the men who manned the ships of war and of the men who had died in the ships of war; whisky there was by the bottle as the great American public, as epitomized by the people on the train, took Jack to their hearts and played that great transatlantic game of who buys biggest buys best. Jack, put there by a helpful Negro car attendant, went to his berth in the middle of the day with all his canvas shot away and his shrouds trailing in the sea of American largesse.

To men accustomed to the pitch and roll of ships, and the never-ending view of empty horizons, the journey across America had been breathtaking and magnificent in its grandeur and sense of immensity. The skies had been blue, the autumn sun warm, and all had contributed to create a never-to-be-forgotten picture of this great and fertile land.

For the Professor these things were but a part of his memories of that journey; on the eve of arrival in New York he met a girl or, more precisely, a woman; he was reading *Mein Kampf* given him by a tipsy host in San Francisco, and was deeply engrossed in this blueprint for Teutonic success when she spoke.

'Mind if I set down?'

He had no objections.

'Jeesus!' She whistled, catching sight of the book with its yellow jacket and swastika. 'An' by thet guy too – an' in Joyman – brother, that's a dirty book here!'

To recognize the German was not difficult, but she was not, he discovered, of that extraction; she said she was 'jest plain American, and paw wus American, and his paw an' his paw's paw, too, I guess.'

They discussed the multiracial society; the United States was held up as mankind's greatest achievement in the sphere of peaceful coexistence. Eve, for such proved to be her name, and the Professor talked of many things on the run in to New York; of England and America, about black men and white men, about the Navy and travel, about love and life and about people generally. The meeting was beset with pitfalls; pitfalls of the flesh; Eve was, in a fluffy thirty-five years oldish sort of way, a very attractive woman. She was also intelligent. The sort of shrewd intelligence which lies behind a veneer of superficiality. They talked about her reason for travelling, a visit to her sister, and about her home on Long Island, and about her husband; he was in the automobile business in a big way: 'Made a pile o' dough.'

Their acquaintanceship ended all too soon as the train reached its destination. 'Ring me, Honey!' she made the Professor promise he would. 'Mickey (her husband), would not be at the station, – he never is – always too goddamned busy!' A kiss, a chuckle and with swaying hips and an over-the-shoulder smile she tripped lightly off the train. A good body, pert, attractive, somewhere between thirty-four and thirty-eight years of age, you can never tell with these American women, and with immaculately coiffeured blonde hair, blue eyes with just the right amount of eye shadow, full-lipped mouth, and the whole set in a round face atop beautifully moulded neck and shoulders, and wearing a smart, refreshingly severe grey costume suit; she was a lot of woman and, as he had just discovered, she wore no foundation garments, or needed any.

Grand Central Station was all hustle and bustle and noise and teemed with cosmopolitan humanity; shoeshine here, paper boys there, porters and baggage and great hissing locomotives, and everyone was in a tearing hurry; the speed and hum of the place was bewildering, and everything was on a vast scale, a great cathedral of a place.

The sailors from *Orient* stood astonished amidst this vast chaos until to their relief they were rescued by the familiar figure of a British Petty Officer who had been sent to meet them; belted and gaitered, very smart and all efficiency, he played to his American audience; he bawled: 'Right, m'lads, – hupbagan'ammicks – gotta truck outside!' The American accent was, it appeared, contagious.

Bagan'ammicks were duly hupped and humped, and the truck rolled from the station on its long, threading run to Brooklyn Navy Yard. Skyscrapers, towering storey after storey into the Manhattan sky, turned the streets into canyons and frowned down upon the seething, antlike activity about their base; necks craned for a glimpse of the Empire State Building, the Chrysler Building, and all the other monuments to the industry of man which composed the fabulous Manhattan skyline, and a sense of wonderment and awe prevailed in the crawling, stopping and starting, gear-changing and horn-blowing truck as it threaded its way through the vortex of the city traffic. So this was New York! Above the roar of the traffic the American sailor who was driving hollered over his shoulder: 'Broadway, fellas – Times Square, yew guys – Central Park thataway an' Park Avenoo!'

Madison Avenue, the Brooklyn Bridge, Flatbush, De Kalb Avenue and all the other streets and avenues, and the river; trolley buses clanged and clattered, the elevated railway thundered overhead, horns blared, drivers cussed, policemen snarled disapproval at the city's driving habits, and New York, afoot and vehicle borne, grinned and waved a welcome to the wide-eyed sailors who in turn waved back and alternated between goggling, gasping, and wolf-whistling. 'Suck back – look at 'er! I'd give me tot fer a munf to screw that!'

At last Brooklyn Navy Yard; easier, said 'Rabbie' Burns, the Petty Officer one-man reception committee, for a matelot to enter the Kingdom of Heaven than to get into the Navy Yard; security was strict but, once inside, the new arrivals stayed aboard their new, temporary home, HMS *Somerset*, an old friend of the days in the Mediterranean, just long enough to unpack their kit, shower, shave and climb into their No 1 suits and steam ashore again to ride the complicated trolley bus and underground system *en route* to Broadway, Times Square and the bright lights and promise of this glittering Mecca; as a seductress beckons, so beckoned New York, and Jack strapped his skates on: 'Testicles, spectacles, wallet an' watch. Hiyup there, Broadway, 'ere we come!'

Chapter 8

Home for Christmas

'As you begin to know something about sailors, have you not often heard, that salt water and absence always wash away love?'

Captain Horatio Nelson to Mrs Nisbett. 19 August, 1786

No matter how tortuous the route, or how devious the path, Jack has an infallible knack, a nose, for getting from point A to point B with remarkable facility and a minimum of fuss; getting from Brooklyn Navy Yard to Times Square in an hour flat was no mean achievement. But Johnny Thomas; 'Nosey' Parker, Engine Room Artificer; 'Sharky' Ward, Leader of Stokers, and the Professor did just that.

After several practice runs, the serious business of the night, they decided, would start at Jack Dempsey's Bar and, for the second time that day they found a welcome amidst the chromium plate, gleaming glass and row upon row of tempting bottles. The resident band, Bob Crosby and the Bobcats, played the latest hits; 'Baraminovitch and His Harmonica Rascals' had everyone in fits of laughter, Angie Bond played the piano accordion, and the barmen dispensed booze as if it was the eve of a new era of prohibition.

'Wadya hev, boys? – this one's on the house.'

Bourbon on the rocks, with a Budweiser to chase it, and cheers to Mr Dempsey; and before they could put away the first drink the barman was setting them up again.

'Genelman over there.' He nodded, and they raised their glasses to the 'genelman over there.' 'Mud in yer eye!' he called.

The second round was barely drunk before the drinks were set up again, the medicine as heretofore prescribed, and a heavily-built blonde with a prow like a man o' war raised her glass in silent tribute from where she sat at a table over-looking the well in which the great oval bar was set. Her heavy jewellery flashed, reflecting the light as she moved, and her well-made-up face cracked into what was intended to be a seductive smile. Before long there was more drink on the bar than they could ever hope to cope with, but, manfully, they waded through it, and ate plate after plate of the crispy pretzels with which the bartenders plied them.

The Professor gripped the bar as it took a ninety degree turn to port and keeled over alarmingly, the bartenders appeared in duplicate, if not triplicate, and the side tables revolved giddily; it was becoming increasingly difficult to draw wind, and his friends were in like plight, they were all foundering upon the rocks of American hospitality; and, as yet, they had not bought a single drink between them.

The buxom lady with the flashing jewellery was now standing at the bar coaxing 'Nosey' Parker and, as if from a long way off, the Professor heard her saying: 'Aw c'mon, honey – ah'll be real nice ta ya – first off we can hit a spot I know, 'ave us a liddle drink an' then go back ta my place – it's real nice – won't cost ya a cent.'

Her intent eyes searched 'Nosey's' face; he reacted slowly but favourably to her suggestion and made one or two counterproposals. She laughed coarsely. 'Why shore, honey – shore – anything yew want, lover boy – c'mon, let's get outa here!' And with drink-slurred excuses to the rest of the party who by this time were at the back-slapping stage in Anglo-American relationships, 'Nosey' and his inamorata left the bar.

The others, now reinforced by four American sailors whose backs they had been slapping, faced up to the task before them with resolution, and invited their new-found friends to help them out with the imposing array of drinks lined up on the bar.

As in all well ordered communities it was inevitable that differences should become manifest; not for long could the British Fleet be left in undisputed control of the seas, and to redress the balance and to justify their existence the American sailors, with no battle experience to their credit, called for ship to ship comparisons, and high-flown phrases such as 'fire power', 'weight-propulsion ratios' and 'treaty restrictions' were bandied about. The controversial ice weathered a bit thin when 'relative merit' was introduced, and the whisky-laden atmosphere became charged with inflammatory elements when the size of fleets was allied to economic factors; here the Professor sailed in home waters, and he gave an inebriated exposé of the British Navy's use as an instrument of political and economic pressure. He excelled himself; certain economic and political malpractices of the Americans were given an airing, and this brought the atmosphere dangerously near to flashpoint. All might have been well if the called-for retraction had been given, but there was no stopping the Professor; were it not for the British Fleet there would never have been an America. America's ingratitude, apropos of the fact that she had not yet declared war, to the country which gave her birth and helped to nurture her to adolescence, he could not with conviction say adulthood, made him spew! That did it! The explosion came in the form of a swinging fist that flattened the Professor's nose all over his face.

'Why, yew goddamned dirty Limey bum!' howled the obviously aggrieved owner of the fist, and every eye in the bar jerked in the direction of the quarrel. 'Yew goddamn sonuvabitch!' The Professor nursed his nose and left it to Johnny Thomas to plant one on the attacker, and this Johnny did, straight between the eyes; the two navies manoeuvred for position, further blows were struck and the crowd in the bar rose to their feet for a better view and to enjoy the fight. One of the American sailors lifted his hand to the back of his blue jean collar, and there was a momentary flash of naked steel, but the knife was never used; it dropped between the feet of its wielder who gave a howl of pain and gazed at his shattered wrist; the barman replaced the still intact bottle on the shelf whence it came and came around the front of the bar to lend further assistance if need be and to help sort matters out. The bouncers employed by Mr Dempsey were big and expert, and the 'bum's rush' is a quick and efficient method of disposing of trouble. The revolving doors had barely ceased to revolve before the banshee wailing of the prowl cars was heard close at hand and, as they growled to a halt at the kerbside, the Professor sat on the paving stones of Broadway nursing a broken nose and a bruised backside and vainly tried to bring a waving nightstick into focus. Wielding the admonitory nightstick was a stern-faced policeman who from his vantage point standing legs astraddle, gazed down contemplatively upon the trio of blood-bespattered and battle-scarred matelots:

'Foightin' is it.' A statement not a question.

'Foightin' so y'are – an' yew fresh from the whaars an' all – Are ya not ahfter 'avin had enough foightin'?'

The law answered its own question: 'No ye 'aven't – well, well, well – an' we're ahfter not takin' koindly ta foightin' in Noo Yark so we're not – I guess we'll all 'ave to be takin' ye in so we will.' And take them in he did, so he did.

The sleek entities of shiny, black and white steel and chromium plate that were the prowl cars pulled away from the kerb, one up town with the American belligerents, and one downtown with the British; the curious crowd dispersed about the business of the 'Great White Way' and in no time at all the Professor and his shipmates found themselves entering the portals of Central Precinct, that grey citadel of retribution which lies on 21st Street. Here was a vast tomb of misdemeanour, appropriately named the 'Tombs' where a garish blaze of electric light was reflected from the dirty yellow walls of rooms and corridors strewn with posters; and, in a small room furnished with four chairs and a table, the criminals took stock of their situation. Everything had happened so fast; one minute they had been having a quiet drink, minding their own business, well almost anyway, and the next minute, almost before they could say 'same again, barman', bang! They were in clink! The Professor's suit was spattered in blood, the others had an assortment of bruises, and all were dishevelled; they were not a pretty sight; they gazed around at the bare walls, at the barred window and at the door which they had already discovered was locked, and they were not happy.

'Sharky' Ward, full of lower deck compassion and concern for the sorely afflicted, looked at his friend and shipmate the Professor and said: 'Christ! Looks like yew wus 'it by a bleedin' bus!'

John Thomas clucked his condolences: 'Or bleedin' sumfin.'

'Right place ta get a bleedin' snoutin',' solemnly opined 'Sharky', 'Jack bleedin' Dempsey's uv all places – bloody good job 'e didn't snout ya personal!'

'Sharky' and Thomas chuckled, the Professor grinned painfully; then, after a long contemplative silence: 'Bet that long, scrawny bastard wot started it all got a beautiful brace uv shiners by now.' Johnny Thomas surveyed his skinned knuckles ruefully.

'Drew 'im orf a right proper goffer (punch) yew did, "Tomo",' ruminated 'Sharky'. 'Right between 'is bleedin' eyes!' He chuckled with relish, and then his thoughts shot off at a tangent: 'Wonder wot 'appened to that dirty, lecherous bastard uv a ERA?'

'Prob'ly shacked up wiv the big blonde 'orse by this time, I 'spect.'

'Didn't fancy 'er.' 'Sharky' shuddered. 'Proper butch – prob'ly strap one on an' screw 'im afore the night's out – don't fancy big birds meself.'

After what seemed an age the same policeman entered the room and motioned them all out; in fear and trepidation they followed him into the maze of corridors and down into that bizarre dispensary of just and equitable retribution: the New York Night Court.

Came the turn of the sailors, and the judge condescended to sit upright and show a little more interest in the night's proceedings; he glowered down from his bench, and the charge was read.

'Foightin' was it? Tut, tut, tut.' He shook his head sorrowfully. 'Foightin' indeed!'

'Suck back!' ejaculated 'Sharky' Ward *sotto voce*. 'Another bleedin' Irishman!'

'Silence!' bawled the big Sergeant. 'Ye'll address yer remarks ta 'is 'onour da judge!'

'Foightin' indeed.' Again His Honour shook his head regretfully. The apprehensive trio quaked in their shoes. His Honour then delivered of himself a lecture upon the evils of drink and the 'dhivil o' the bhottle'. This was followed by the inevitable question: 'Y'are not fra t'owld counthry are ya?' He then cross-examined them on the way the war was going 'out there' made a few uncomplimentry remarks about 'da lousy Joymans' and permitted himself a wintry smile; at the smile the sailors' hopes rose, the judge beamed and hopes rose higher; then the judge frowned a juridical frown, and hopes plummeted.

'Lock 'em up!' he barked, and hopes hit an all-time low.

In the long bare corridors below Central Precinct the open cagelike cells cast the menacing shadow of bars on the naked concrete of the floor; with a metallic clang the door of the sailors' new, and they hoped, temporary home was locked behind them, and they stood in the middle of the cage and gazed about like a trio of souls lost in the shades of purgatory.

After a dejected, austere night or morning, to be more precise, at six a.m. the cell door opened.

'Roight, me bhoyos, come wid me.' Another bloody Irishman!

They followed him through a labyrinth of corridors, swing doors were pushed open, and they found themselves not back in court being surveyed from the pinnacle of American justice, but in the canteen of Central Precinct; here they were plied with ham and eggs, hot rolls and coffee, and a friendly cigarette to round off the best breakfast they had had in a long time. The patrons of this early morning repast, policemen to a man, were most friendly and helpful. After the meal they were led back to the court; but there was no judge this time, just a friendly Sergeant who, grinning, said they had been locked up for their own good; New York after dark was no place for drunken sailors; he gave them another lecture on the evils of drink and, with a friendly handshake, sent them on their way.

Thoroughly chastened and wiser men, and with nothing but gratitude for the 'foine gennelmen' of the New York City Police, the by now stone-cold sober sailors returned to their ship, conveyed thereto in a police prowl car; and, as a special treat for the exclusive benefit of his distinguished passengers, the driver kept the siren going all the way to the dockyard gates.

One day the Professor 'phoned Eve, and in the weeks that followed he shared his time between her and runs ashore with the boys; but as their relationship ripened she grew more and more demanding. Both their parts in the affair were dictated by sheer physical gratification; they suffered no illusions about that. They would walk and talk on the avenues and boulevards of New York and Long Island: now basking in the autumn sun on the beach; now riding in a mad whirl of flying skirts and screaming laughter on the machines of Coney Island's funfair; now in Central Park, or on a ferry across the Hudson River; now at Eve's home on Long Island Sound. They became inseparable, and Johnny Thomas went on his way and said nothing, and waited for the day when it would all end.

High summer was passed, the north winds bared the leaves in Central Park and the cabbies donned their mitts and scarves and put a blanket on the horse; aboard the British ships speculation was rife as to the chances of arriving home in time for Christmas.

Out upon the broad bosom of the North Atlantic, just down the river past the Statue of Liberty, the convoy battles raged and grew more bitter by the day, and the sight of wounded merchant seamen on the streets of New York bore testimony to the intensifying U-boat campaign. The news on the radio sent a chill through the messdecks of HM Ships which lay in the Hudson River; down there, out past Staten Island and Long Island Sound, lay the Atlantic and the U-Boats, and that was the way home.

6 December, 1941 was a day just like any other in New York; the city teemed, and the scurrying millions went about their affairs without much thought for the world which lay beyond the Manhattan skyline. When darkness descended the lights went up on Broadway, Times Square and Park Avenue, and the city gave itself over to relaxation and Saturday night's pursuit of pleasure. Dawn broke and, as usual, caught its inevitable quota of late night-early morning revellers wending their belated way through the never empty streets; and then, as dawn broke and the city returned to life, the news broke with a force that stunned the nation, the whole country reeled from the shock of Japanese treachery and a Fleet destroyed at Pearl Harbor. By nightfall shock had turned to anger, a deep and abiding anger; an anger which demanded retribution; an anger which, in the bars and on the taxicab ranks, in the hotels and on the metro, in offices, shops, factories and homes, became a clamorous demand for vengeance. America declared war.

But there was bad news of the British Fleet. All through the summer months sinkings had been heavy. When a destroyer, sloop or corvette was sunk on the convoy routes it was seldom reported; it was largely a matter for grief amongst the families and the sailors who had known these gallant little ships and their companies; but when a big ship 'bought it' it was news, and the nation sorrowed. The battleship *Barham* had been sunk only a few weeks before; in Alexandria harbour the battleships *Valiant* and *Queen Elizabeth* had been badly damaged by Italian frogmen using limpet mines; in the Far East Singapore had fallen and the battleships *Prince of Wales* and *Repulse* had been dive-bombed to extinction. These were grievous losses, and the men of the fleet felt them badly.

It was against this background that the Professor and Eve said goodbye at the gates of Brooklyn Navy Yard; no tears, no fuss, just a dry-eyed acceptance of what had to be. 'And no letters, honey. But, if you are ever in New York again, look me up.' A fair-sized slice of at least one man's life was left behind to wave farewell from the Battery as the cruiser *Somerset* cleared the narrows at Staten Island and lifted her bows to the great, rolling swell of the North Atlantic. The Statue of Liberty faded astern in the swirling mist, the Manhattan skyline was no more, and America was lost to view; no lingering looking astern, no slowly receding coastline to look back at; the mist which rolled in from the Atlantic's watery waste obscured all that and, as the foghorns moaned, someone voiced the sailor's farewell: 'Well, ther' she goes, Scouse me ol' flower – one turn of the screws pays all debts.'

The Royal Naval Barracks, Devonport, were as grim and forbidding as ever on a cold day in late December. Johnny Thomas and the Professor walked towards the Joining Office with requests for leave clutched tightly when Johnny stopped suddenly and said: 'A few more steps an' we are back at the window.'

'What bloody window?'

'The Drafting Office window uv course.'

'So what?'

'Don't yew see? When we reaches that window we'll 'ave circumnavigated the earth! We started from 'ere nineteen months ago – these few steps will complete the circle!'

'Well I'm buggered. So they will!'

And solemnly the two friends linked arms and paced off the steps: 'Five, four, three, two, eureka!' They whooped, they clasped hands and shook on it and it was then that the Professor made his proposal.

'We've come a long way together, Johnny. What say we try to see it through to the end together?'

Johnny pumped his friend's arm.

'Prof – yew got yourself a deal – sink er swim we'll go all the way – shouldn't be difficult – always volunteer, swap drafts wiv somebody, er work a fiddle – a pound note or tin o' ticklers goes a long way in depot.' Such was the price of a draft chit.

Since the death of his parents the Professor was homeless. As Johnny's parents had offered him a home, he went home for Christmas with his friend, and Mrs Thomas fussed over her two sailors like a portly ministering angel. It was Christmas Eve when they arrived, and Johnny found that, apart from wartime austerity, little had changed: Mr Thomas senior still sat before the fire, shoes off, braces dangling and sucking a cold pipe; the two younger Thomases had been shooed off to bed stuffed to bursting point with chocolate brought home by big brother John and Uncle Prof; and Gwen, younger by two years than Johnny, washed dishes in the kitchen, her shapely legs luxuriating with the caress of brand-new nylons brought all the way from New York.

All was peace in the Thomas household: the fire burned cheerfully, the blackout curtains lent an added degree of snugness in the room and, comfortable in slippers and flannel trousers, Johnny and his shipmate took their ease with feet on the fender.

Jack was home for Christmas.

Chapter 9

Yankee 'four-stacker'

'My good fortune seems flown away.
I cannot get a fair wind, or even a side wind. Dead foul! — Dead foul!
Vice Admiral Lord Nelson to Alexander Ball, 19 April, 1805.

Christmas leave, as did all leaves, passed all too soon. The journey back to Devonport had possessed the nightmarish qualities of all such journeys in those bitter days of total war; freezing cold, standing room only, fitfully dozing in the draughty corridors, tightly pressed in the confined space, a long delay at Bristol for an air raid, a further delay at Exeter for a troop train and an eventual arrival at Plymouth hours late and half dead from hunger and tiredness.

During the time that Johnny and the Professor had been away the barracks had not changed one whit, and they were even more crowded; hammocks were slung so tightly together that there was scarcely enough room to get in and out, and no room to turn over once turned in.

Air raids were troublesome, but it did not need eight thousand men to protect the barracks; this was a job for the Passive Defence Party at which everyone took a turn according to Standing Orders, Sitting Down Orders, and all other orders, and always ready to run for shelter if the need arose.

The intercom crackled all day and every day as lists of names of men on draft were read out, each man to report to the Drafting Office 'at the double' if not sooner; and at THE WINDOW the queues grew longer as each day grew older.

'Martin-Smiff!' barked THE WINDOW.

'Aye, aye!' barked the Professor in proper seamanlike manner.

'Yer y'are.' And THE WINDOW flourished a slip of paper under Martin-Smiff's nose. 'Draft chit!'

'What's *Chippenham*?' the Professor stooped to enquire.

THE WINDOW glared at him who dared to enquire thus.

'Yew bastards is all the bloody same,' snarled THE WINDOW. 'Can't yew bastards go on draft wivout a lot uv damnfool questions? Time enuff to worry about that when yew gets there – start yer draft routine afore I slaps yew in the rattle (Commander's Report) – fink I got nothin' better to do than stand yer all day tellin' a bunch uv silly sailors where 'tis they'm goin' to!'

'Next!' bawled THE WINDOW.

In the queue was a Leading Seaman who was only too willing to supply the required information: 'Bloody good Christmas present she was – wouldn't 'ave that pig's orphan agin fer all the bubbly in the Andrew (rum in the Navy).'

'What is she?' enquired the Professor politely.

'What is she?' repeated the Leading Seaman laughing. 'What is she? Well yew might ask what she is, mate – she's the dirtiest, leakiest, rollin'est old tub whatever put ta sea. She ain't a ship – she's a bleedin' submarine!'

The informant found the look on the Professor's face funny, he laughed uproariously: 'Well, not 'xactly a submarine though she does a sub (substitution) fer one.' He laughed again at his unintended pun. 'No mate – pullin' yer leg – she's one o' they Yankee four-stackers – yew know, one o' they ex-Yankee destroyers – four-funnelled bastard!' He snorted his disgust. 'Ten knots a stack me fuckin' eye – bloody lucky if she makes ten knots flat out!'

Comprehension dawned; so he was going to one of President Roosevelt's 'Trojan horses' ships which were on the side of the enemy; floating scrapheaps. Well, well, well! The Professor, like everyone else in the Navy, had heard all about them; they were renowned throughout the service, for all the wrong reasons; no one had a good word to say for them; they were poor sea boats, they were topheavy, 'shipped it green' (took in water) in any kind of weather, and rolled atrociously; sea water and oil fuel floods in the messdecks were every day occurrences, the seas often put out the galley fire and, consequently, their ships' companies spent half their lives living on corned dog (corned beef) and hardtack; and, because they were flush deckers, their upper decks were untenable in heavy weather. Their only armament was a couple of Oerlikon anti-aircraft guns, and an aged 4-inch gun mounted on the fo'c'sle which unshipped its moorings and destroyed the Captain's cabin every time it was fired. Such were the stories which circulated through the Fleet, and no one doubted their truth.

Johnny Thomas was not perturbed by his friend's news and, because of their pact to stick together, volunteered for *Chippenham*. He was not allowed to volunteer because he was already on draft to Mombasa; but he could, and did, swop drafts; Mombasa for *Chippenham*, East Africa and sunshine for the cold and misery of the North Atlantic. It was an easy matter to effect the swop; no one wanted the ex-Yankee four-stacker.

Four days later, in company with some hundred and fifty others, a complete ship's company, the two friends entrained for Cardiff and their new ship. The city was drab and fogbound in the light January drizzle, the streets around the docks were cold and uninviting, and the ship itself was in little better plight; evidence of dockyard tenancy was strewn about her decks; she was drab in dirty camouflage, and with large areas of rust disfiguring her like some scabrous disease; she had no steam in her boilers, and dockyard workmen swarmed everywhere; scraping, hammering, riveting and drilling like a swarm of demented bees, and the 'windy hammers' set the ship to shuddering from stem to stern.

Only two of her officers were 'proper RN', the others were 'Wavy Navy' 'bloody Saturday night sailors' of the Royal Naval Volunteer Reserve or wartime conscripts. Of the two proper RN officers one was not really anymore, even though he had been to Dartmouth and commanded a destroyer in the 1914-18 war. In the early thirties Lieutenant Commander John Henry Justice had felt the weight of the 'Geddes Axe' and, like so many others in those days of shortsighted parsimony had been 'chopped', that is, kicked out. In civilian life he had been doing very nicely thank you, selling advertising space; he now commanded *Chippenham* as a full Commander, and already had a DSO and bar to his credit; he had no complaints, not now; in civilian life he had held a job which paid him handsomely, and now he was back doing a job he loved – commanding a destroyer; a dirty old tub of a destroyer, a floating junkyard maybe, but a destroyer for all that; and at sea she would earn her keep, or he would know the reason why not, so he said.

The First Lieutenant, to quote 'Nutty' Mills, 'Queen of the fo'c'sle' (Petty Officer in charge of the sharp end), 'was as popular as a bleedin' grass snake in a barmaid's droors!' Also proper RN he had gone through Dartmouth at about the same time as his Captain had been presented with his bowler hat, and he was not a popular man. 'James' (Jimmy the One – First Lieutenant) was a fixer: 'I'll fix you for this, Able Seaman. Crash!' And he was also a slave driver, could cuss like a dockyard matey and was by general consensus a proper nasty piece of work.

The rest of the officers were acceptable, young and inexperienced and green behind the ears, but they would learn the hard way. The doctor was a man apart: completely and utterly mad, he drank like a fish, threw the most abominable parties and was reputed to be a lecher of high accomplishment; a man of parts indeed, a man to be respected. He was young and far too good looking for his own good; the product of some obscure Scottish academy, Oxford, Guy's Medical School and two years as a destroyer's 'quack'. It was rumoured that he would 'Whip summat outa ya as soon as look at ya, and kick yer ass outa the 'chancre locker' (Sick Bay) if 'be fawt yew wus workin' a flanker!' There were also two Warrant Officers on board: the Chief Engineer, Royal Naval Reserve, and the Gunner (T) (Torpedoes), and they lived somewhere in limbo between the Wardroom Mess and their place of duty; not quite respectable enough for the Wardroom; too bloody respectable for the messdeck!

In early March *Chippenham*, all shipshape and with a new coat of camouflage, left Cardiff, and her ship's company were glad she did; certain ladies of the Principality were getting too possessive, and the slates in the pubs were a trifle over-chalked; it was time to up anchor and away.

From Cardiff into the Irish Sea, St George's Channel, and so to Tobermory, there to 'work up' and take part in the dreaded evolutions again. Nothing had changed since the last visit of the Professor and his friend John Thomas, Able Seaman; these islands off the Scottish coast were still bleak and barren, certainly no place for any self-respecting matelot; wild, windswept, rain-lashed, and inhospitable, and no place for a proper run ashore unless one liked the company of sheep.

Work-up completed, the ship sailed south on the short haul to the Pool of Greenock; the Captain attended a convoy conference in the Commodore's ship, and *Chippenham* already stored, fuelled and ammunitioned was away on the evening tide. The convoy formed up off Ailsa Craig and steamed south-west for the Mull of Kintyre and north-west about into the North Atlantic. Fussing, cussing, marshalling and cajoling, the shepherds of the escort went about the business of forming up the convoy in some semblance of good order for the run across to Newfoundland; pitching and rolling in a rising sea the escort fanned out to take up station on the outside of the flock and the oddly assorted conglomeration of ships settled down to a steady ten-knot plod to the west.

John Henry Justice suggested that a certain, rusty old tramp keep station in a proper seamanlike manner or he would save a U-Boat the bother and ram a torpedo up his arse himself, and the Captain of the tramp told him, in words which blistered the paintwork, what he could do with his torpedo! In the starboard lookout position, in the wing of the upper bridge, the Professor listened to the verbal exchange, grinned and enjoyed himself immensely. The ol' man was quite a card until the old man caught him looking inboard and grinning. 'You won't find any U-Boats on the compass platform Martin-Smith – eyes out ta bloody sea man – eyes out ta sea!' It was alleged that the old man had eyes in his backside; he could certainly see around corners, and he could see slacking lookouts skulking behind any one of the ship's many funnels, and he gave them all a bollocking just for starters; he started as he meant to go on; he would make '*Chippers*' the most feared escort in the North Atlantic or die trying.

So different, thought the Professor, from the ultra-efficient *Caucasian* with her equally efficient if somewhat puritanical Captain. The Captains were as different as the ships they commanded. Perhaps, he thought, therein lies the reason why one was axed and the other was not: just a passing thought on the qualities that go to making a good destroyer skipper.

The North Atlantic was bitterly cold, the sky was grey and heavy with rain and sleet squalls, the wind blew with increasing velocity from the north-west, and the squalls obscured the ships from sight of each other and set the standing rigging humming like some devilish chorus; a heavy blow was imminent and *Chippenham* lived up to her reputation; she rolled and pitched with a bad, irregular motion and did her utmost to prove that she was a wicked sea boat and that the gossipers had not been kidding; there was not a scrap of grace in her. As the sea whipped up and grew angry her masthead traced a crazy asymmetrical pattern against the blackness of the low-scudding cloud; wave-lashed she surged forward into a head sea, her decks awash from stem to stern, and every time she hit a 'milestone' (wave) she shuddered and her plates creaked. Rolling, pitching, stalling and veering, she crested the waves with bows spewing water and overhanging their spume-garnished tops with half the ship's length out of the water and, with sickening, stomach-wrenching, corkscrewing plunges she slithered down into the troughs and up the other side to repeat the performance. Eccentric; now falling away, now righting and shaking herself like an angry terrier, now lifting her bows out of the sea, now her stern so that her screws thrashed empty air; but, despite all that the Atlantic threw at her, she maintained her station on the convoy's northern extremity.

On the bridge and on deck the watch, miserable, forlorn and cold, and often wishing to lie down and die with seasickness, huddled into their duffle coats and oilskins and thought bitterly of warmer, more hospitable places; home in front of Ma's sitting room fire, a pint in a cheery local, or the soft, twining arms in some feather bed.

Below decks the air was heavy and humid despite the cold on deck, and fouled with the smell of bodies that lived in close proximity; the smell of wet clothes, stale food, spew, sweaty socks and a hundred other unnameable odours, was nauseating. Suitcases and mess utensils crashed and clattered around unsecured, a foot of oil fuel and water swished back and forth over the heaving decks and, amidst this squalor and disorder, lay the 'couldn't-care-less' and the 'lay-me-down-and-let-me-die', jammed in among the permanent fittings to prevent themselves being thrown around and injured.

During the evening of that first day of the storm the 'Chef' was also jammed into a hurt-proof position in his galley; with doors and portholes dogged down to keep the light in and the storm out, he cursed roundly and dreadfully. In his hot little haven he toiled manfully over the preparation of supper: soup, stew with dumplings, and boiled potatoes in huge iron pots secured to the top of the galley range with iron 'fiddles' (retainers) to prevent their sliding off and scalding their custodian to death. 'Don't suppose the bastards'll want to eat it anyway!' he mumbled. But the Chef never said die; nineteen years in the Navy and never seasick in his life, he had no sympathy for those who were prone to the malady of the sea. 'If they wus too bloody sea spew, or too bloody bone idle, to come an' get it they could bloody well 'ave corn dog an' 'ard tack – er bloody well go wivout!' But the Chef would still brave the elements to go round, hanging on to the lifelines for dear life, with a steaming hotpot of soup or 'ki' (cocoa) for the lookouts or anyone else who fancied a cup of something hot. It took more than an Atlantic gale to put Chef Pollard, one of the Navy's unsung heroes, out of action. 'Sailors,' he spat, 'I've shit 'em!' It was his favourite expression. 'Then shit another un' Chef, an' I'll go on leave!' said one of the peasantry and got a swipe around the ear for his audacity.

Night came and the Professor, recently promoted Leading Seaman, and 'Killick' (Leading Seaman) of the Watch on Deck, had the middle watch (midnight to 0400); he always took the starboard side of the compass platform; it was his perk and a place which could easily be covered when he had to leave to check the Watch. The night lay heavy, pitch-black and full of menace, the storm was at its worst and he shivered in the biting cold and lashing rain. Thank God, he thought, this weather'll keep the U-Boats down; that, at least, was some consolation for the discomfort of the night. The Captain was on the bridge, where he spent most of his nights; if circumstances permitted he slept in the mornings and catnapped in the afternoons; if circumstances did not permit, he went without sleep – all part of the burden of command. In the wheelhouse, illuminated only by the small red glow of the compass card light, the Professor mustered the watch; outside the storm crashed and raged, inside all was snug and the quiet response to names called was the only sound apart from the noise of the storm and the occasional repeat of course from the Quartermaster: 'Course red two-o, Sir – midships – wheel amidships, Sir,' in response to orders down the voicepipe from the bridge above.

'Christ! – but this bastard rolls, an' she bucks an' kicks like a bloody mule!' 'Jacky' Kingswood, the Quartermaster, spat his disgust and drew upon the cigarette which his mate the Prof had just placed between his lips when that worthy lingered for a 'few spits an' a draw' before going back out to face the madness of the night and the lonely vigil of the Watch on Deck.

'Who's up top with the ol' man? asked the Professor.

'Jimmy.' There was a wealth of expression in the one word.

Then, apropos of nothing in particular, he said: 'Wet bastard!'

Came the voice of the First Lieutenant down the voicepipe: 'Did you say something, Quartermaster?'

'No, Sir.'

'Hm, – thought you did.' Number One sounded unconvinced, then snapped: 'Pay attention to the wheel – hold her on course – and only proper servicelike responses up the voicepipe, please!'

'Aye, aye, Sir!' 'Jacky' peered into the suffused, red glow of the binnacle: the course was spot on.

'Daft as a brush,' he mumbled.

'Kingswood – stop muttering!'

'Aye, aye, Sir!'

In the darkness 'Jacky' grinned; Jimmy was his pet hate and the feeling was reciprocated. 'Jacky' was clever, competent and a fine seaman who was qualified for direct promotion to regular commissioned rank; he was a 'bread and butter' sailor. His clash with the First Lieutenant was one of personalities and he held that worthy at bay by sheer ability and the clever use of that old Naval expedient known as 'keepin' 'is nose clean'.

Day followed day and the convoy struggled to the west, and on the sixth day the Professor again had the middle watch, and still the storm raged, and the night was as black as only a storm-ravaged night in the North Atlantic can be. On the upper bridge, exposed to the elements, he clung to the bridge surround and strained his eyes into the night; was it imagination or had he heard something; a faint noise in the storm; a noise that should not have been there; a noise that had nothing to do with raging seas and howling winds? He had a feeling, a sixth sense, that something was wrong, something was about to happen. Suddenly he stiffened and sensed rather than saw the First Lieutenant who had been standing in the port wing of the bridge, hurl himself across to the voicepipe and in a voice that came hard and frightened in the darkness he heard him scream: 'Wheel hard astarboard!'

Faintly came the surprised response of the Quartermaster: 'Wheel hard astarboard, Sir!'

Surprised, yes, but his response to the order was immediate and unquestioning, and in one dreadful, frightening moment the Professor knew what had happened or what had almost happened; he knew that the faint noise which he had heard had been the noise of another ship, the thumping of her engines all too audible now, and a great black mass, blacker and more terrifying than the night, slid slowly down the port side; there came a sickening, grinding, scraping noise as both ships rubbed together and he tensed for the next terrible rending and grinding that would send *Chippenham* plunging to the bottom. But it never came; both ships parted without further contact and both went their way into the night. How the pitching, rolling, wave-lashed ships had failed to collide only God and the night would ever know; when the ship had responded to helm those on deck had grabbed the nearest means of support and, as she keeled over at an alarming angle, prayed to Almighty God for deliverance from the raging sea. The danger passed, below deck the pandemonium subsided and on deck the Professor found himself sweating from sheer fright. It had been a near thing.

On the bridge the Captain who had been having a smoke in the charthouse, spoke softly: 'Thank you, Number One'. Just that and no more. The First Lieutenant's honour among men was assured for all time and the ship sailed on through the night.

The Med, thought the Professor as he strained his eyes into the night, had been bad enough; the dive bombers and the battles had been enough to frighten the shit out of anybody, but this you couldn't fight; this incredible sea, this weather; no man had control over this and he fell to trembling.

The Damage Control Party, led by the First Lieutenant, reported that the ship was not in a bad plight; there had been no casualties, a boat had been carried away, a few stanchions were bent, a few plates sprung and she had lost a lot of paint; otherwise she was sea and actionworthy and would do until she got to a dockyard. The sheer size of the merchantman had saved her; it had been a clean scrape down her unencumbered side plates.

Two days later the storm abated; the convoy awoke to a calm sea and a clear sky, and the business of rounding up the convoy began. Some of the ships, storm-driven, had scattered over hundreds of square miles of ocean, but were gradually brought together; others were never rounded up and proceeded to Halifax independently, and some fell prey to predatory U-Boats. The storm had put the convoy behind schedule; instead of being nine days steaming to the west they were, by distance covered, a mere five days west. To start with the convoy had been only a 'ten knotter' and the storm had reduced this to about five knots, and now they were in the middle of the most dangerous part of the crossing; it was here, in the 'black hole' that the wolf packs lurked and awaited their prey.

The day the storm abated was one of those amazing days that from time to time the Atlantic throws up; a beautiful day, a day of sunshine, calm, cold and clear, and with peerless view to the far horizons; a day potent with the menace of U-Boats.

The Professor, leaning over the berthing rail and watching the sea go washing and sploshing down the ship's side, thought of birds; there ought to be birds on a day like this, birds that chirped in trees, and spring flowers too. Nostalgic memories of before the war came flooding back; blue skies, birds in trees, spring flowers and long walks through St James's Park and Hyde Park, or down the river to Mortlake and Kew and on towards Richmond. Since joining the Navy he had reached man's estate in the hard school of war at sea; a man can learn a lot about himself out here on the oceans. He thought of home, and he thought of Mum and Dad, a luxury which he deliberately tried to deny himself these days and his eyes misted. Angrily he turned to where Able Seaman 'Arry 'Awkins and some of the hands were supposed to be busy about the business of making good some of the damage done by the merchantman.

'Whatsamadder with yew loafin' bastards – paralysed?'

They grinned at him, that infuriating grin of the matelot who has no intention of being pushed around.

He relented and laughed: 'Lazy bastards – c'mon, get on with it – get that boat in trim or I'll 'ave yer guts fer garters!'

Walter Pater Martin (bloody hayfen) Smith was very much the Leading Seaman these days; he had swapped doctrinaire economics for the Manual of Seamanship.

'Too bloody quiet fer my likin,' said Johnny Thomas who was one of the party. 'They rotten U-Boats is pro'bly ganging up on us right now – right down there.' He pointed a significant finger down at the turmoil of the sea.

The Professor gazed out upon the concourse of ships in company; cargo vessels, tankers and ocean liners on the trooping run; westward-bound for the Americas, North and South; to Panama and via the canal to New Zealand and Australia, or bound for the same places via the eastern coasts of the Americas and round Cape Horn. Big ships and small ships, and tramps with crabby paintwork; forty-five ships in all – they had started with sixty; ships which flew the flags of a dozen nations, and eight escorts; two of which were ex-American four-stackers, two sloops, and four corvettes of the 'Flower' class. Not a very impressive escort, but the best that could be scraped together in these dark days.

Suddenly from *Chippenham*'s starboard lookout there came a shout: 'Torpedoes running green five-o, Sir!'

The Captain looked over the side at the fast-approaching torpedoes and took no evasive action; he could see that they were not meant for his ship; he judged that they would pass astern, and they did; into the convoy sped the 'kippers' and up their tracks sped *Chippenham*, flat out at a full eighteen knots. Pattern after pattern of depth charges were hurled over the side from the throwers or rolled over the stern from the traps; dull underwater explosions told of their detonation and the surface of the sea bellied pregnantly before the columns of water shot upwards. Eager eyes scanned the surface of the disturbed water for sign of oil, debris or, vain hope, a surfacing U-Boat.

Back in the convoy a tanker was down by the bows and blazing furiously and a fat-bellied tramp rolled over and disappeared beneath the waves with her screws still turning. Another dull roar, another sheet of flame leaping skyward and another ship was sent to the bottom, blown clean in half and folding like a jackknife as she went. The escorts tore around in a frenzy of counterattack; they quartered the area, dropped pattern after pattern of depth charges, and the morning wore on to high noon, and still the carnage went on and ship after ship went to its grave on the bottom of the ocean.

By the time darkness came the casualties were twelve; twelve ships sunk in one day and no U-Boat killing to claim; it was a heavy price to pay. Somewhere around 24 degrees west the convoy was handed over to the Newfoundland Escort Force; casualties had risen to fourteen, and one U-Boat for certain; the eastbound convoy was picked up without delay, and *Chippenham* and her consorts headed for home. It had been a bad run, the escorts were laden with survivors of whom *Chippenham* had her share, and wrecks of men some of them were; maimed men, and men with their lungs being slowly eaten away by oil fuel; men who breathed with a harsh, rasping sound and coughed up blood and membrane; men who had not a hope in hell of ever seeing home again and who would be honoured with a White Ensign for a burial shroud and find their last resting place beneath the ocean over which they had fought. And so it continued for month after deadly month.

But life on a destroyer on the Western Approaches was not without its lighter moments; for instance, the occasion when, in mid-Atlantic, the destroyer *Foxhound* ran out of depth charges and it was decided to replenish her at sea by Light Jackstay Transfer. Both ships were rolling rather badly in a long, lazy swell and it promised to be a bit tricky; the lower deck was cleared of all hands and, grumbling and cursing most foully, they were 'piped' to man the Jackstay falls (ropes); then there was played a hilarious game of tug o' war to take up the slack or ease the strain as required by the man in charge of the operation, namely Jimmy Green, the Warrant Gunner (T) who, owing to his lack of stature, was known throughout the ship as the 'Little Green Man' or the 'Kipper Bosun' or 'Torps'; anyway, mounted atop the port flag locker on the bridge, and facing aft, and clinging to the Aldis lamp mounting for dear life, he bawled his orders couched in good old-fashioned navalese through a hand-held megaphone.

'Right, me 'earty tars – take up the slack – TAKE UP THE SLACK! – adsamadder with yew bastards? – said take up the slack! – 'andsomely, 'andsomely – right, me lovely boys – walk aft, walk aft – stamp an' go, me beauties – walk aft – WALK AFT! – WALK AFT YEW DAFT BASTARDS! – stamp an' go! – Pickle me mother's chitterlings! – did yew ever see such a gormless shower?'

The hands stamped and went, and gave the 'Kipper Bosun' a chuck up (cheer).

'Avast 'eaving – AVAST 'EAVING! – that means stop, yew clowns – stop – whoa – 'old 'ard – pay out the falls – PAY OUT THE FALLS – COME FOR'ARD – this way, yew idiots – up towards the sharp end – belay the falls – BELAY THE BLOODY FALLS – stop paying out – STOP PAYING OUT – take the strain – walk aft – stamp an' go! – c'mon, can't none of yew bastards sing? – let's 'ave a sea shanty!' and he started the refrain himself:

'I met me a gal in Plymouth town,
Mark well what I do say.
I met me a gal in Plymouth town,
Her eyes were blue, and her hair hung down,
And I'll go no more a-roving for you fair maid.
A-roving, a-roving, for roving was my ru-i-in...'

The hands joined in the shanty with gusto and, one after the other, the depth charges were swung outboard to ride the alternately slackening and tightening wire which spanned the chasm between the two ships.

Suddenly the inevitable happened, the wire went taut, the depth charge spun around it, flew off the strop and dropped between the ships; there was a concerted rush away from the sides of both ships.

' 'Salright, 'salright!' howled the 'Little Green Man' through his loud-hailer, 'Yer perfickly safe; she ain't primed or set fer depth!'

Of course she was not primed or set for depth – ha, ha, ha! Not much she wasn't! B-o-o-o-o-m! Both ships shuddered, the sea between them swelled like a pregnant duck, a great spout of water shot skywards, everyone was soaked to the skin and the 'Little Green Man' was accorded the biggest chuck up of his career to date. The Captain spoke strong words in the ear of his Gunner (Torpedoes) who, in his turn, spoke even stronger words to his Torpedo Party; great was the gnashing of teeth 'midst the tin fish tribe.

In *Foxhound* they had joined in the fun at the falls and in the singing, and a good afternoon of sport and skylarking was had by all concerned; during the transfer, when the ships rolled apart, it had been possible to see *Foxhound*'s keel. She, likewise, had been able to see *Chippenham*'s keel; when the ships parted to take up station again, the latter made a signal to the former: 'Thank you for the party. Did you know that you showed your bottom every time you rolled?'

Came the reply from *Foxhound*: 'Don't be disgusting. Do you know that your bottom needs a shave? We have never seen such barnacles. Thank you for the wherewithal to continue the struggle, and please convey our condolences to your Gunner (T).'

Chippenham was pushed until her engines screamed in protest; the summer drew to a close, and once again was joined the ageless battle with the winter gales and driving sleet of the North Atlantic. The Chief Engineer, Warrant Engineer James Bertrand Armstrong, 'Louis' to every man in the ship, was a hard-pressed and sorely tried man and he pushed his ERAs and stokers as hard as he pushed himself. He attributed his latest crop of prematurely grey hairs to his playing wetnurse to the ship's temperamental and clapped out 'ironmongery'; he had almost forgotten what it was like to spend an undisturbed night in his bunk or to sit down to a meal in peace. It was strongly rumoured that the ship was to be docked in Liverpool in December for an extensive refit; home for Christmas became the watchword, and the ship's company cheered to the echo every time the engines ground to a standstill; even so it was not funny to sit around without power in U-Boat-infested waters in mid-Atlantic.

By early December the ocean had assumed its indecorous winter mantle – lashing rain, sleet, snow and high seas driven by winds which howled straight off the Arctic icecap; it was then that *Chippenham* really earned her crown of laurels and staked her claim to a place on the Atlantic Roll of Honour.

It had been a particularly vicious, eastbound convoy from Halifax, with all the attendant horror and tragedy without which no day was complete, and ship after ship had been sent to the bottom by predatory U-Boats; and the greatest tragedy of all was that these eastbound convoys were laden to the gunwales with supplies for beleaguered Britain, had come from the four corners of the earth to the Halifax rendezvous and were on the last leg of their journey home; this convoy had been made worse by the loss of three of the escorts.

With nothing to show for her efforts *Chippenham* had carried out the usual number of fruitless searches and depth charge attacks, and had been ordered by the senior officer to sweep well astern and to north west of the convoy. She had completed her sweep and turned to rejoin the close escort, disappointed, frustrated and without as much as a 'ping' to show for her labours when, suddenly, from the after lookout position, a cry was raised. 'U-Boat surfacing dead astern, Sir!'

And there she was. The action klaxon sounded, men rushed to take up their action stations and a great air of excitement reigned as the ship came about in a tight turn to see the submarine rising from the depths like some ocean monster, with water cascading down her ominous black hull. The ship's company went wild. At last something to have a crack at! No more running around in circles, no more chasing tin cans and shoals of fish – real, live U-Boat on the surface!

Obviously the U-Boat could not dive or she would have already done so; she was on the surface because she had no choice in the matter. On *Chippenham*'s bridge the Captain knew precisely what he was going to do; many times over the past months he had worked out his mode of attack for just such a situation as this. He would use his 'peashooter', the 4-inch gun which graced his fo'c'sle, and with himself bows on to the target and coming up fast he would blow his adversary out of the water. His bows were not reinforced, but, if all else failed, he would ram her and to hell with the consequences; if he lost his ship in the process, well, it would be a fair trade; this dirty old four-stacker for a U-Boat.

'Shoot the bastard! – Ram the bleeder! – Sink the fucker before she dives again!' Feelings ran high on the convoy routes. No quarter was given and none asked for.

They need not have worried; the U-Boat would not dive, she couldn't; *Chippenham*'s depth charges had not all been hurled away in vain. Orders from the bridge came down to the Professor who was laying the 4-inch gun on the fo'c'sle. He licked his lips in anticipation, his heart pounded with excitement and, with the realization that it was all down to him, he swore at the Canteen Manager for nearly dropping a shell on his toes when the ship rolled, yelled at the Killick Steward to pull his 'fuckin' finger out' and squinted anxiously into the 'spider's web' gunsight. Here was the opportunity of a gunlayer's lifetime; it was all completely down to him. None of your fancy electric fire control and direction-finding nonsense with this gun. All good 'handraulics' (a pun)!

Up went the revolutions as the Captain rang down for full speed, and round came the ship in another tight turn that nearly sent the gun's crew slithering across the exposed deck and over the side; as it was, the Killick Steward, who was the ammunition number, dropped the 'projjy' (shell) he had been hugging to his chest like some jealous mother hugging her newly born, onto his toes and his howl of anguish nearly frightened off the U-Boat.

There she was in the sights – range 1,000 FIRE! Missed, and the bang nearly wrecked the bridge superstructure. Short, and the range closing fast – range 800 – FIRE! – Missed; over the top, and there was a tinkling of broken glass from the Captain's cabin which was right behind the gun. Range 500 – can't miss this time – this is fairground stuff – C'mon 'Damager' (Manager) ram that bleedin' projjy up the spout – FIRE!, and with his third shot the Professor did not miss. Slap in the middle, right underneath the conning tower, but not before the U-Boat had also got a shot in; wha-a-a-e-e-e-u-u-u-h, that weird, bombarding sound again; half scream, half moan and *Chippenham* had a hole in the top of her for'ard funnel. It was the last shot the U-Boat would ever fire; the shell she had taken in her hull had done enough damage; she was keeling over to port and in a great flurry of bubbles and the hissing of escaping air she was sinking fast; her crew, in inflatable, yellow lifejackets, scrambled madly out of her for'ard hatch and leaped into the sea to strike out madly in their endeavours to get away from their doomed boat.

In a matter of minutes and with a last despairing gurgle, she was gone; the cheer raised from the cock-a-hoop ship's company of *Chippenham* was a bitter pill indeed for the Germans who struggled in the water where once their boat had been.

The Professor was the hero of the hour. 'Bloody good shootin', Prof.' It had been classical shooting in fact; one short or should it have been over? One over or should it have been short? And one spot on, and that, despite every thing the Manual of Gunnery preached, did not have to be anything but a hit. 'Good ol' Prof! We showed the bastards!' Everyone was jubilant; they nearly pummelled a hole in the Professor's back and in that of the Canteen Manager and the Killick Steward; the Professor was the only seaman and Gunnery Rate in the gun's crew.

'I hope you realize,' the Captain commented with a laugh, 'that you have completely wrecked my cabin!' And he was dead right: as the Killick Steward, whose domain it was, confirmed 'The bleedin' place is a pot mess (stew) – this is it Prof – 'ome fer Christmas, matey – even the for'ard bulkhead's buckled!'

After the third shot had struck home *Chippenham* had slewed under hard helm a-port; this to avoid collision with the submarine, and to avoid ploughing into her survivors. She slowed and came about; it was too risky to stop for long; the fact that she was picking up survivors from a sunken U-Boat was no guarantee of immunity from attack by other U-Boats. Scrambling nets were put over the side, the survivors were assisted aboard and in a matter of minutes she was under way again, steaming at maximum speed, all eighteen knots of it, to rejoin the convoy.

Standing with backs to the berthing rail amidships, the survivors looked anything but a sorry bunch; bedraggled yes, soaked to the skin and with chattering teeth, their yellow lifejackets standing out in stark relief against the dull, grey Atlantic backdrop; defeated no, they looked defiant, with eyes that challenged and with sneers on their faces. Two ABs from the gunner's party had been hastily armed with Lanchesters and now stood guard over the prisoners; the Gunner (T) brandished a service .38 revolver under their noses, and they were searched for concealed weapons, hand grenades or anything else with which they might do somebody a mischief. Nothing was found. To a man the ship's company gathered around and with ill-concealed curiosity stared at these representatives of the master race who in turn stared back defiantly and one of them spat contemptuously; but for all the response he got he might just as well have saved himself the trouble; Jack laughed at him, and this disconcerted him far more than a rifle butt in the guts would have done.

Speaking fluent German the Captain addressed the prisoners; he said they could now regard themselves as prisoners of war and in conformity with the Geneva Convention would be treated as such; if the Captain of the U-Boat would kindly step forward and make himself known he would be treated with the courtesy and respect which befitted his rank. There was no Captain. If any of the Officers would care to step forward they too would be treated with the respect and courtesy due to an Officer. There were no officers. If, then, any of the Chiefs and Petty Officers would come forward they also would be treated as their status demanded. There were no Chiefs and Petty

Officers. The Captain gave it up as a bad job; there was no Captain, no Officers, and no Chiefs and Petty Officers, and no one spoke English or, for that matter, German. He turned away with a shrug. 'Put 'em down below, Mister Green.' And down below they went.

And, as the Captain turned to leave for his bridge, the spitter, as smartly as his stockinged feet and shivering body would allow, stepped forward, clapped his heels together soundlessly, flung out his right arm in the approved manner and shouted: 'Heil Hitler!'

Jack laughed again; someone mentioned something to do with gentlemen's private parts and someone else shouted: 'Chuck the bastard back in the drink!'

'Topsy' Turner, Able Seaman and resident comedian, took a pace forward, snapped the heels of his seaboots together smartly, flung out his arm and said in the approved manner: 'Heil Churchill! – an' up your fat ass, yew Kraut bastard!' Everyone except the Germans thought it was screamingly funny.

Herded down into the non-steaming boiler room the prisoners were given blankets and hot soup, the doctor was sent down to minister to their medical needs and sentries were posted to keep a round the clock watch over the boiler-room hatch. Big-hearted Jack gave them cigarettes, and they were fed twice a day on 'pot mess' and 'hard tack'.

The Professor remembered the pride that all had felt when the Captain was awarded a bar to his DSO; three DSOs in one war can't be bad; and his own embarrassment, pride and amazement, when the Captain had announced that he, Leading Seaman (Temporary) Walter Pater Martin-Smith, Royal Navy, had been awarded the Distinguished Service Medal: the Professor, DSM! That had been the toast of the messdecks; you could have knocked him down with the rum fanny! The Leading Steward and the Canteen Manager had been 'Mentioned in the Canteen Chit book' (Mentioned in Despatches); there had been something to celebrate, and the Professor winced every time he remembered his hangover.

Mine host of a certain well known pub where the '*Chippies*' had celebrated was used to such goings-on; since 1939 he had helped to wet many a 'gong' and was adept at catering for the needs of vanquished heroes. The Professor had awakened next morning, as naked as the day he was born, in mine host's back bedroom, his clothes folded in a neat pile at the bedside; his arrival back on board at about ten-ish of the clock in the forenoon had been greeted by a cheer from his shipmates, and the Officer of the Day had turned the Nelsonic eye as the latest addition to the honour's list had staggered back on board. What a night! What a head! And no, he had not seen that louse of a Killick Steward, or the Canteen Damager either. 'The bastards were probably sleeping it off somewhere – shacked up wiv some bird more like!'

With leave in prospect they eagerly went their way to the barracks at Devonport, to the formalities of getting into the place, and the fearsome procedure for getting out again. Every time they, or anyone else, requested leave they were always met with the same stock phrases: 'Leave – leave did yew say – wadya want leave fer? – Anybody ever tell yew bastards there's a war on?'

'Yes, Chief – we 'eard a buzz to that effect.'

'Don't be bloody cheeky – yeryar – travel warrant an' leave pass – fourteen penn'orth – don't be adrift.'

They had heard it all before. Eagerly they took their 'liberty tickets' and eagerly they travelled north; eagerly for the Professor because of Johnny's sister, and for the promise that had lurked in her eyes.

The train was packed with eager sailors all going on leave; there was much fun and high spirits and there was singing of many songs:

'Yew could tell that Jack wus 'ome again,
An' 'e wus doin' fine,
For there wus 'er frilly knickers 'anging on the line,
With 'is dirty, great kidney-wiper,
An' 'is knackers swinging free,
An' 'alf a yard of foreskin 'anging down below 'is knees'

Chapter 10

Yankee Land Again

'The service must ever supersede all private considerations....Do not repine my absence.'

Captain Horatio Nelson to his wife. 3 October, 1794.

Christmas Day, 1942, faded into the limbo of things remembered, the fitful embers of the sitting room fire still cast a warmth about the room where Johnny's family sat around and yawned, and Dad, braces dangling, announced that he was off to bed. Mum fussed around for a while and, with an over-the-shoulder admonition to the children not to be too late, followed him up the stairs. One by one the family retired, including Johnny, who knew that he would only prove an embarrassment if he stayed longer.

During the first few days of leave the Professor and Johnny's sister had spoken little; they divined each other's thoughts; the time for words would come later. There was between them a charged current of knowing, a sense of waiting for the inevitable, a mutuality of tension; now they were alone, sitting in opposite chairs and facing each other across the fireplace.

Johnny's sister put more coal on the fire, poked at it until it started to blaze, got up and switched off the light, and came to sit on the settee which had been drawn up before the fire.

'Come and sit here, Walter.' She patted the settee at her side. He was finding it strange to be called by his Christian name, but she refused to use any other; he did as bidden and in silence sat beside Johnny's sister and gazed to where the flames were doing battle with the fresh coals and as the flames grew in strength he conjured visions from their flickering; visions of boyhood and innocence and memories of other Christmases, and his heart was sad to breaking. Sad, bitter and alone, his very soul cried out in protest at the injustice, the stupidity and the pointless sacrifice of innocent people and tears rolled down his cheeks. It was the first time he had cried since that day when the Captain of *Caucasian* had broken the dreadful news of his parents' death.

At his side Johnny's sister had been watching him intently. She stretched out her arms and took his face in her hands: 'I know,' she said tenderly, 'I know.'

And drawing him to her she kissed his tears and wondered at their saltiness.

He looked at her and studied her face, and she returned his scrutiny with steady gaze. In many respects she was like her brother; blonde hair, blue eyes, slim of features and with a dimple in her chin and with a good figure with long, shapely legs. Pretty and at this moment the most desirable thing in the world; he wanted her, and yet was afraid to touch her; after all she was Johnny's sister. His pulses raced, his heart pounded and the blood surged through his temples. The tenderness in her eyes was an invitation, a demand, and suddenly they came together in a passionate embrace; her arms pulled him close, their mouths met and they sank into the settee. He kissed her again and again; her lips, her eyes, her face, her neck and down into the vee between her breasts and, holding him close, she returned his passion in full measure.

'Darling,' she whispered, 'I thought you would never get around to it.' And again and again: 'I love you. I love you, darling. I love you, love you, love you.' And for the thousandth time he kissed her, abandoned and passion-driven.

'I love you, Gwen darling – love you, love you, love you – I love you with all my heart.' He knew that for the first time in his life he was really in love and, submerged in the glory of that love, they spent the night before the sitting room fire and their passions knew no bounds.

The cold, grey light of dawn filtered through the cracks in the blackout material; Gwen kissed her sleeping lover tenderly and, pulling an outdoor coat over her nakedness, she poked the fire into life, put on some more coal and went into the kitchen to make tea. To the waking Professor there came the sound of cups clinking in saucers, Gwen humming a popular tune and the evocative aroma of freshly brewed tea. Returning with the cups she put them down, and he tenderly removed the coat from about her and pulled her to him and kissed her breasts, ran his lips over the flatness of her stomach and down into her pubic hair; she pulled him to her again and they made love again.

Eventually they rose from their love making and, handing him a cup of cold tea, she said: 'A toast, my love, a toast in cold tea.' They laughed together.

'What shall it be?' he queried tenderly.

'To us – a toast to us.'

Ten minutes later, from the hands of a radiant Gwen, the whole family received a cup of tea in bed, and Mum and Dad gave each other a meaningful look. For the lovers the remaining days of leave were halcyon days, but days clouded with the dread of the parting to come.

It was a dry-eyed parting for Gwen and the Professor; Johnny's mother shed the tears for all of them, and the journey back to Devonport was purgatory. Johnny and his friend spoke little; Johnny could see how the old Prof was feeling and respected his silence and, silently, the Professor damned the war, damned the Navy, and was generally speaking not a happy man. RNB Devonport was worse than ever; more crowded than ever, the queues were longer, the food no better, and draft chits flew as thick as the leaves of autumn.

Twenty-four hours after joining the barracks, Johnny and the Professor appeared at the Drafting Office window; their tentative query to the oracle elicited the usual, sympathetic reply:

'Leading Seaman Martin bloody hayfen Smith!' barked the oracular consultant.

'Here, Chief.'

'Don't yew bloody well call me Chief. I ain't no Chief. Flattery'll get yew no place yer!'

'Able Seaman John – Christwhatanandle! – somebody 'ad a sense uv 'umour when they started yew down the slipway, Thomas.'

'LST One,' the consultant continued. 'An' if yew asks me wher' 'tis I'll kick yer bleedin' teef in.' Said with a complete lack of emotion.

Then, as an afterthought: 'Tell 'ee the truf I don't know meself – one o' they 'ush 'ush jobs.'

Drafting cards were marked to the usual offices, and one particular pencilled cross immediately caught the eye of Johnny Thomas: Tropical Clothing Store.

'Looks as if we'm goin' foreign, Prof,' then, with emphasis, 'Again.'

Four nights later, pulling out at midnight, special trains left the barracks' railway siding, loaded to the gunwales with mystified sailors, and headed north, destination unknown. Over the whole operation there prevailed an air of secrecy, thousands of men had been detailed for these drafts, LSTs 1 to 15, and all that anyone knew about them was that tropical kit was deemed to be necessary. Speculation ran rife. 'Prob'ly clew up up the Norf Pole, 'count as 'ow we got issued wiv soddin' tropical kit!' The perversity of Their Lordships was a never ending source of lower deck humour; if tropical kit was issued you could bet your sweet life you ended up on an Arctic patrol; conversely, if duffle coat and seaboots were the thing to take on draft it was a copper-bottomed certainty that the Persian Gulf would shortly be extending a sub-tropical welcome. So opined the messdeck *cognoscenti*.

With the coming of the dawn Bristol it was, and there, drawn up on the platform, was a large contingent of Royal Air Force personnel who, judging by the blue rings around their kitbags, were also bound for foreign parts. This was too good an opportunity to miss; from the train there were hoots of derision, jeers, catcalls, hisses and wolf whistles, and every sailor on the train joined in the baiting of the 'Bloody Brylcreem Boys.'

'Caught up wiv yew loafin' bastards at last, 'ave they?'

'Bloody Brylcreem Boys!'

'Go to sea, yew bastards!'

'Get some bleedin' time in!'

'Does yer muvver know yer out?'

Downright insulting they were; ribaldry was the thing; insults and taunts were hurled back and forth across the station until the very domed roof of Temple Meads rang with the clamour. Someone remembered the bag meals; packed with such loving care by the Chief Cook and the galley peasantry at RNB Dev, and which contained amongst other delicacies 'tiddy oggies' (Cornish pasties); most excellent oggies they were, too, produced to the highest Jago (dining hall) standard, all golden brown and crimped of back, like baby dinosaurs, and filled with meat, veg and rich brown gravy; designed by a benevolent Paymaster to allay the pangs of Jack's hunger on the long journey to wherever it was he was going; but what excellent ammunition, what missiles!

Splonk, – splonk, – splonk! Surprise registered on the faces of the RAF draft, consternation reigned and they wiped meat, two veg and rich, brown gravy from their faces, scraped 'clacker' from their tunics and brandished their fists at the cheering matelots; loud and long the laughter and the station staff stood well out of range of the flying oggies and thought the whole thing rather funny. The RAF might have been conspicuous by their absence over Malta, Greece, Crete and the North African coast from Tobruk to Benghazi, but that was the fault of vacillating politicans and inept brass hats; never let it be said that here, on the battlefield of Bristol, Temple Meads, they went down without a fight. After the initial surprise they fought back and hurled what was retrievable of the oggies back at Jack; but the sailor fought from a strong strategic point; he closed the windows, and the train pulled out, its coaches bespattered with clacker; two veg, meat and rich brown gravy.

Hereford, Shrewsbury, Crewe, Carlisle and Carstairs and it became evident that the draft was Glasgow-bound; when the train clanked to a halt under a sign which proclaimed 'Port Glasgow – Docks' there was no doubt about it and, after a lot of shunting and shoving, it eventually came to rest alongside a great, grey ocean liner which belched smoke lazily into the cold January air.

On the dockside it was bitterly cold and everyone welcomed the activity and bustle as kit was unloaded from the train and piled into nets before being swung by crane into the liner's holds. Soon everyone was trooping up the long gangway and into the warmth of the ship; and there in the vast, confusing maze of her interior they were sorted into messes and were allocated the all important, slinging billets for their hammocks. Breakfast was served in a dining room which had once known the lilting refrains of the liner's string quartet; here in these great compartments, drab now and denuded of past glory, had been heard in the days of not so long ago the tittle-tattle of polite conversation, the peals of laughter and chink of elegantly stemmed glasses, held with the equally elegant cocked little finger. 'Would modom care to try the Canard en Chemise? And perhaps monsewer would care to try the Chateau d'Yquem '34 – a delectable and enduring little wine – such a delightful nose, monsewer.' Jack was a passenger and he revelled in his new found status and soon settled into a regular routine of eating, sleeping, reading, writing letters and playing cards; there were some very naughty poker schools going; or standing all innocently and with a studied nonchalance that fooled nobody beneath the ladders which led to the women's quarters; here he could help the ladies up or down, always the perfect gentleman, but preferably up so that he could do his eyes a power of good with the odd glimpse of a suspender belt or the merest flicker of frilly knickers and the odd few inches of thigh.

In the evenings there was the cinema, 'sod's operas', all local talent and good for a laugh, and the old troopship favourite – a nightly singsong; a very clean singsong of course; there were ladies aboard, who, although they might appreciate the lyrics of the 'Lobster Song' in private, could hardly have been seen to do so in public. The noise mattered not at all, the ship was too fast to worry unduly about U-Boats, and it was not U-Boat weather anyway – dead foul. Jack was in his element whilst all about him spewed; if he wanted two suppers he could have them, and did; three breakfasts with three eggs apiece and a dozen rashers of bacon – a mere snack; and on the day of embarkation, at about seven bells in the forenoon watch, Jack was electrified into feverish activity. 'Up Spirits' was piped over the ship's tannoy; strictly for the naval contingent of course; civvies and soldiers did not qualify. Jack cheered himself silly, the ghost of Nelson stalked abroad, and the matelots mustered with their little tin mugs in the hallowed presence of the rum fanny and received from the hands of the ship's Purser a tot of 'neaters' – 'none of your watered down stuff. Cheers, oppo – sippers, Jan boy – down the hatch – ah-h-h-h – not a bad drop o' bubbly that.' Someone decided to chance his arm and 'go around the buoy' (take a second helping) and it worked; the word got around and everyone took a quick nip around the buoy. O what a swindle! What a wheeze! 'Skin off yer nose, "Yorkie" – mud in yer eye, "Scouse" – Bloody good ship this bastard!' But Jack's little racket was short-lived; someone in the Purser's Office deduced that if there were one thousand sailors aboard the ship then they should have consumed one thousand tots of rum, not two thousand, and that, due consideration being given to the fact that there are such strange creatures as teetotal sailors, was a generous estimate. Next day the heavens fell and all was gloom and despondancy – there was no rum. This measure was taken to make good the loss of the previous day, and the following day Jack was required to hand in his Pay and Identity Book; no Pay Book, no tot. 'Swindle it wus – proper bleedin' swindle. Crafty bastards these bloody Pursers!

Despite delays owing to heavy seas, it was not long before Nova Scotia loomed out of the Atlantic murk and *Empress of Scotland* nosed with grey majesty to her moorings. On deck the passengers huddled into their overcoats, pulled their woolly comforters about their ears, shivered in the bitter cold and looked with curiosity out upon the snow-covered landscape; white as far as the eye could see, a vast sheen of white broken only by the house and factory frontages which peered from out the snow like enigmatic faces with expressionless eyes. The watchers in the ship shivered the more and shrank deeper into their coats – by God it was cold.

On the dockside, manoeuvring a long line of Pullman cars into position alongside the ship, a great Canadian Pacific 'coast to coaster' snorted and puffed like a prairie buffalo. The monster eventually subsided into hissing and belching inactivity, and it was time to go; the baggage was swung outboard and the sailors beavered away at sorting their kit and loading it aboard the train. The naval draft left the ship first; this was exclusively their train and on the dockside it was a case of emulating the beaver or freezing to death on the spot; 'Pusser's (Service issue) Burberries, overcoats and bags of tropical kit were poor protection against the Nova Scotian winter. 'Didn't I tell ee, "Scouse"? Yew gets issued wiv bleedin' tropical kit an' yew clews up up the norf bleedin' pole!'

All was at last ready and after an hour of pure agony whilst they thawed out the sailors settled into the warmth of the train and, with a mighty snorting, a puffing and a deep-throated wailing, the huge locomotive gathered momentum and pulled its long string of cars clear of the docks.

Dawn and sailors have a preordained rendezvous – a destiny; and dawn was breaking as the train pulled into Grand Central Station, but there was to be no disembarkation in this vast metropolis of sleepless souls; the train was shunted, backed and shunted again; the engine was changed and eventually it pulled out on the last stage of its journey. A bridge over the river; Newark, New Jersey; Jersey City and at last the travel-stained and weary sailors disembarked, and there before them was their destination; two towering, luxury hotels, sybaritic twins, the hotels Berkeley and Monterey. 'Bit uv a change from Jago's, "Scouse"!' There were even lifts, elevators in the local parlance, to take Jack and his bag and hammock to any one of God knows how many floors. No doubt about it, these Yanks laid things on in a big way.

No Card Hut, no Guard Room, no gates and no duties to speak of; Jack never had it so good, and the Jossman couldn't care less: 'Cos 'e wus up 'omers too – 'ad a bird in Brooklyn.' The sailors came and went more or less as they pleased, and it usually pleased them to stay 'went'; but if only to catch up on some sleep, Asbury Park made a good place to come home to now and then.

To revisit old scenes and renew old acquaintances the Professor changed ready to step ashore, and looked forward eagerly to the proposed trip to town; to Broadway again, Central Park and Times Square and he might even pop in to see Jack Dempsey again; after the year which he had just spent on the Atlantic convoy run he felt he owed himself a little relaxation, a small measure of letting down the hair. How long the drafts would stay in America was anybody's guess. The last year had been hard and bitter; when they did leave it would be to return to the war; it was a case of enjoy life whilst you can and to hell with tomorrow.

Adjusting his collar he gazed at himself in the full-length mirror – such luxury! He smiled at himself and admired his reflection – such vanity! It's the uniform that does it – such pride! He adjusted his cap tally. He viewed himself sideways and frowned; trousers a shade too low – he hitched them up a bit; a twist in the arm seams of his jumper – he straightened it; a pat here, a pull there, silk a wee bit bulky – he flattened it. By Christ but you're a good looking bastard! – an' all the nice girls love a sailor. Girls. He frowned at himself again; Eve, what of Eve? Should he look her up? He thought also of Gwen. He thought of Gwen and he remembered Eve, and thought of Eve and remembered Gwen. Damn it! Of course there could never be anything between him and Eve again, not after Gwen. No, his mind was made up; he would not look up Eve, not ever, not even for old time's sake. God, he thought, who the hell are you kidding? What had old time's sake got to do with it! Eve was a very attractive woman and she was bloody marvellous in bed.

' 'urry up, Prof, yew good lookin' bastard – yew'll do,' shouted John Thomas from the full-length mirror at the other end of the room – such spaciousness. 'We gotta train to catch.' Which indeed they did, from Asbury Park to New York. 'Doc' Henry, otherwise Herbert George Henry, 'Pox Doctor's Clerk' or, officially, Sick Berth Attendant, poked his head around the door of the room.

'Come on yew tiddlivating pair uv brown 'atters, shake it up. We'll miss that bleedin' train otherwise.'

'Who's fer a jar?' The 'Doc' was dry. His thirst was renowned. In civilian life he had been a commercial traveller; how that profession qualified him to be a Sick Berth Attendant was a mystery vouchsafed only to Their Lordships, in their legendary wisdom. And in pursuit of his daily bread he had acquired a strong predilection for the hard stuff. All three were in complete accord and repaired unto a hostelry hard by the entrance to the station.

W-a-a-a-ah, w-a-a-a-ah, w-a-a-a-ah! From down the line came the wailing of the Pennsylvania Railroad Company's 'Limited' from Pittsburgh, or some such place. 'No panic – mud in yer eye, "Doc" – cheers, "Tomo"!' Came the clanging of the train's departure bell. 'Git yer bleedin' skates on, blokes!' A mad, hundred yards' sprint; the way was barred by a black and white steel pole across the level crossing; the trio took the barrier like gazelle clearing bush and pounded up the platform after the moving train; Johnny jumped for the observation platform at the end of the last car and made it. The Professor also jumped and landed safely.

'Come on, Doc – yew'll make it – run, yew bastard, run – jump, Doc, jump!' The 'Doc' jumped and did not make it; instead he landed in a heap on the line astern of the speed-gathering train.

'"Doc's" 'ad it – "Doc's" 'urt – Jump, Prof, jump!' They both jumped in unison, rolled down the bank at the side of the line, picked themselves up, dusted themselves off and started back down the line to render assistance to the smitten 'Chancre Bosun'. Sober they would have been killed or at the very least done themselves a mischief, but they were intact; not so 'Doc' who lay there and moaned which proved that he was alive. From the station people came running and 'Doc' was carried, moaning in mortal pain, back to the booking hall; came the wail of the ambulance siren and the trio went to hospital escorted by motor cycle outriders from the Jersey City Police Force. The all attentive hospital orderly who accompanied them in the back of the ambulance politely declined their invitation to ' 'ave a wet' from the bottle which by some miracle was recovered intact from the Doc's pocket.

White tiles, white-robed figures, and through the fumes of alcohol permeated the heady smell of disinfectant. 'Doc' was wheeled away on a trolley covered in a white sheet, and very miserable 'Doc' looked, too.

'Bedder keep some fer ol' "Doc" when 'e comes out – hic! Drunken bum – hic! Fanshee 'im fallin' orf a bleedin' train – hic, hic!'

When the 'Doc' did put in an appearance he looked like something akin to an escapee from the mummy department of the British Museum. He remonstrated with the doctor and the nurse, waved bandaged arms in the air and said no in a voice and with a conviction which brooked no contradiction; no, he did not want an ambulance to take him back to Asbury Park. He had come ashore for a run with the boys and a run ashore he was going to have.

'Look after the crazy galoot,' said the doctor; look after him indeed they would, and the intrepid trio tottered from the premises in search of the yet unconquered field. Another train without mishap; then New York's Pennsylvania Station and an empty Bourbon bottle left for the sweeper. By now it was dark, the city blazed with lights and, as the trio walked up 34th Street and turned into Broadway, they huddled into their overcoats against the biting north-east wind, and there was snow in the air. A beer seemed to be indicated and a small enlivener would not come amiss, so they adjourned to a place which the Professor knew.

The 'Doc's' decision to carry on with the run ashore was to prove a wise and profitable one. He was bruised, and he was lacerated, but was otherwise feeling in fine fettle. 'Nuffin' wrong wiv me that a few jars won't fix.' Just how wise 'Doc's' decision was, was proved as soon as they entered the bar to which the Professor led them. The bartender, eyes eloquent with sympathy, looked at the 'Doc':

'Jeez, fella, wadda hell hit ya?' and, before the 'Doc' could reply, three Bourbons on the rocks, 'double whacks' were being pushed across the bar, and the bartender was saying something about it being pretty goddamned rough out there, he guessed.

'Out there? Oh, yeah, out there – yeah, sure, it was pretty rough out there – very rough indeed.' The penny had dropped, light was cast into dark corners and the 'Doc' hazarded a shrewd guess as to where 'out there' was; anyway it always paid to humour bartenders or anyone else who dispensed Bourbon on the rocks – double whacks – free.

Amongst the Professor's last memories of the evening was seeing the 'Doc's' bandaged head sinking lower and lower behind a punchbowl and under the table.

Then Eve's voice saying:

'Wal, Wal, Wal, honey – Hello, Wal darling. Remember me? – It's Eve, honey. Eve, Eve, Eve, Eve, Eve,' from far, far away.

Light filtered through to dark places. A familiar voice, a familiar face which swam in billowing cloud amongst echoing, cloud-clearing mountain peaks. The voice boomed, as booms the roll of thunder. Why did it have to boom so? And why the devil is she wearing hobnail boots?

'Hello, Wal darling.' She kissed his mouth.

'Eve – Eve darling.' He gazed at her in wonder. 'How did you get here – where am I?'

She laughed and told him of how she had found him at a party at 'Jason's place – a neighbour of ours.' She brought him home by cab and put him to bed, as drunk as a skunk.

'Some party eh?' He agreed that it had been quite a party.

He bathed, shaved, dressed and they talked. For her it had been a fortuitous meeting and she marvelled anew. For his part he was not too sure. He thought of Gwen and he thought of Eve. He could look at Eve, touch her, smell her perfume and there was promise in her eyes; but he could not look at Gwen, could not smell her perfume, and as the promise in her eyes was four thousand miles away, Eve won the battle of remembering. Here was Eve, and he did not have to remember any more; he pulled her arms from about his neck, undressed her in the half-light of the still drawn curtains, and gazed upon the mature beauty of her nakedness; drawing aside the curtains to flood the room with light, he took her to her bed.

Outside the waters off Long Island were grey, wind-whipped and restless; across the room on the mantelpiece the ormolu clock ticked away the hours, and Wagner and Beethoven frowned upon their love-making from fluted, columned pedestals. If those stony eyes could see and those marbled lips talk, what could they tell of Eve? He shrugged aside the thought; what did it matter? Eve had not changed. He studied her at breakfast as he struggled with the voluminous *New York Times*. He knew Eve, or thought he did; her every gesture, her every move, her politely coarse jokes and the desire which flickered in the depths of those big, blue eyes. He had spent the remaining hours of the previous day and the night with Eve and his conscience and had found them both very accommodating bedfellows.

It was decided that he would stay for a few days as her husband was out of town, and then she would drive him back to Asbury Park in the car. They would do the rounds of all the old places, and all the old crowd. So it came to pass, they did the rounds and met again some of the old crowd, revisited the old places, talked a lot, drank a lot and made a lot of love while America grew more angry with the war as the days passed.

Back in Asbury Park with Johnny and the 'Doc' notes were compared about that monumental run ashore. 'Doc' was mending fast, but seemed to suffer from a permanent hangover. Johnny had a girlfriend whom he had met at Jason's place and whom he was courting strongly. He was besotted with love and spent half his time shunting back and forth on the Hoboken Ferry; Jean lived in Brooklyn and Johnny disappeared for days on end.

Whilst the LST drafts were living it up in America the Battle for the Middle East raged apace. El Alamein was but a memory; the Eighth Army rolled inexorably to the west, away from the Suez Canal and out of the shadow of near defeat. The hard run and sorely tried Mediterranean Fleet had been relieved; most of it was, or had been, in America for repairs, and now Britain was on the offensive; but it had been a close-run thing and the price had been high.

Days ran into weeks, and the weeks ran into six; the New York hurdy-gurdy churned out its melody of pleasure and the time came to leave. The farewells were said, the tears were shed and the men of the LSTs moved on to join their ships; for such they had proved to be, Landing Ships (Tanks), being commissioned in half a dozen ports on America's eastern seaboard; from Boston down to Philadelphia, and on down to Charleston, South Carolina.

John Thomas and the Professor went to Philadelphia and found strange ships; great, empty shells of ships with flat bottoms and with doors in their bows which opened like the gaping jaws of stranded whales. The Professor, standing on the ramp down which one day the tanks would roll, felt for all the world like Jonah in the act of being swallowed. The ships were empty because the tanks which they would one day carry were thousands of miles away, and no one knew where. East to Africa, or west through the Panama to Guadacanal and the Philippines? On the upper deck of each ship was secured a smaller craft, a Tank Landing Craft, and the Tank Landing Ships looked like great, ungainly whales which had just performed the miracle of birth.

Aboard each ship were two crews; one for the parent ship, and one for the offspring – the Tank Landing Craft. The latter was composed of six men of the US Navy, commanded by a very intense, fresh-faced young Ensign straight out of the Naval Academy at Annapolis. Inside the Senior Officer's ship, the Professor's ship, as with all these ships, the living accommodation was spacious; every man had his own bunk, 'No slingin' yer mick aboard this bastard!' and there were long fore-and-aft passages which ran the length of the ship and which were also lined with bunks which would one day accommodate the tank crews and infantry. The huge empty tank deck, designed to take dozens of tanks, lorries, guns and other vehicles, was possessed of a lift for raising and lowering them to the upper deck. All in all, a very strange ship.

Southward steamed the squadron from Philadelphia, to be joined by all the other squadrons from their shipyards until, by the time they stood off Savannah on Georgia's Atlantic coast, they spread for miles across the ocean; a vast concourse of ungainly, flat-bottomed 'beach scrapers' formed up in columns of convoy for the long haul to wherever it was they were going. They could not afford to hang about in these waters for long; this was U-Boat country; the new happy-hunting ground of the wolf packs; and the escorts fussed and shepherded, cajoled and bullied, hooted and threatened until all were under way and headed in the right direction.

South to the Bahamas, south-east to a dawn vision of the hills of Puerto Rico and the Virgin Islands. East or west? Movements were then broadcast throughout the ships; east it was, east to the Canary Islands, the west coast of Africa and on to the Straits of Gibraltar. Apart from the rolling, pitching and lurching, the crossing was uneventful. But how those ships rolled, how they pitched and how they slapped their flat bottoms and shuddered and quivered like springboards the whole of their length. A horrible motion; they had no keels to allay their ungainly, sickening, sideways slide and heave. On these ships a man needed all his skill and sealegs to stay afoot, and they were routed just north of the equator in order to get the smoothest crossing.

Clearing the Canaries with the frowning mountains of the Atlas to starboard, the ships hugged the North African coast for the last leg of their journey to Gibraltar. Here, there was no shore leave. The LSTs were going straight through to Alexandria, and no one looked forward to the narrow sea. Rommel was not far away, the *Luftwaffe* still held the airfields of southern Italy and Sicily, and the run through held a promise of being fraught with peril.

The attack, when it came, followed the same pattern as of old; first the black speck on the horizon that was the reconnaissance aircraft, immediately followed by 'air attack, yellow warning'; then the shadow boxing with fire circuits tested, magazines manned and the sky-probing movement of elevated gun barrels as crews checked mechanisms and 'dummy-sighted'. 'Air attack, warning red' and all was quiet with the quietness of just before battle; the unearthly silence just before all hell breaks loose. These flat-bottomed barges were no potent men o' war; they did not have speed and manoeuvrability nor the fire power needed to fight off dive bombers; their companies, dry-mouthed and stomachs constricted with fear and dread of the impending assault, stood to their guns and waited.

The JU-87s climbed into the sun, hovered there for what seemed an age and plummeted down upon the ships; but this time things were different, the diving aircraft were met in mid air above the convoy by 'Hurry carts' (Hurricanes) and Beaufighters of the Fleet Air Arm and RAF. 'Here was a turn up fer the bleedin' book, an' no mistake!' Dogfights raged above the ships and ended in the whining, black-smoke-trailing, downward spiral to death in the sun-dappled sea; that day both friend and foe died in the battle which raged in the sky; undeterred, the ships sailed on and the convoy cleared the narrows without damage.

Every time a JU-87 was shot down a mighty cheer was raised from the sailors watching from the ships; when the doomed aircraft was seen to be wearing the British 'bull's-eye' there were groans of abysmal woe. Jack hurled advice skyward, waved his fists at the battling aircraft, if he could see that they were German; there was in the air a heady smell of sweet retribution as the Mediterranean Fleet, proud and triumphant, swept to the east. A new phase of the war had opened; Britain was on the offensive.

Chapter 11

Tank Landing Ships

'Something must be left to chance; nothing is sure in a Sea Fight beyond all others. Shot will carry away the masts and yards of friends as well as foes.' Vice Admiral Lord Nelson from Victory to the Fleet off Cadiz. 9 October, 1805.

Alexandria had changed but little; the vice, the corruption, the filth, the poverty and the noise were still there, and over all still hung the same intangible atmosphere of eastern mystery. But in the teeming hordes of jabbering natives, the pimps, beggars, thieves, traders, and all the other parasites for whom the poor British matelot is legitimate prey, there was a change, and not a particularly subtle one. No longer were they arrogant, boastful and openly hostile; the old cringe had returned, the whine was back in their voices and Jack was once again 'Master'. Rommel was in retreat, and the accursed Ingleesh once again reigned supreme; tomorrow would dawn as all the other tomorrows had dawned since the very beginning of time. Maleesh. What did it matter? Allah, the ever bountiful, would provide.

Meanwhile men went about their affairs unmolested by the *Luftwaffe*; it was a time for a little skylarking, for relaxation and for going ashore on pleasure bent. Mail from home arrived regularly, the food supply was normal and a man could sleep at night without fear of the dawn. Four hundred miles away, in Greece and in Crete, the enemy still maintained a tenuous hold; he was still in Italy and in Sicily, but these days the dreaded *Luftwaffe* seldom darkened the Levantine sky, and the ships that rode to anchor in the harbour of the Nile's delta saw nothing of them; they were far too preoccupied in Russia and, as they retreated to the west across the desert of North Africa, so they retreated in the same direction across the plains of southern Russia. 'Drang Nach Osten' was going home and a quiet confidence in ultimate victory was abroad in the narrow seas.

Aboard the ships whose sole reason for existence was to land tanks on enemy-held beaches life was not so good; of all the ships in harbour their's was the most urgent task; there was work to be done. It had been decreed that if these ships were to be grounded upon enemy-held shore, then their companies must be trained in amphibious warfare; and, if by some frightful mischance, they were not able, in due course, to leave the shore, then they must be taught to fight like soldiers. Perish the thought! But their Lordships of Admiralty, being wise in all things, and especially in the ways of war, insisted; and so it came to pass – it was time for training.

To the west of Alexandria the Landing Ships (Tanks) went to a place called Mersa Matruh, and there, on a barren stretch of beach, they rammed the ship ashore; bow doors opened, ramps went down and off into the blue rolled the tanks, the jeeps, the lorries and the guns which had been loaded for the exercise. Jack had fulfilled his *raison d'être* and for his friends in khaki he was pleased to do so, but things were not to be left at that; off into the blue also went Jack. O fiendish powers which control the affairs of men! O soulless exponents of the art of war! Jack was dressed in khaki and wore a little round hat, and webbing equipment like a proper soldier; he was given a dirty great pack for his back, a water bottle, a rifle, and, indignity of indignities, a pair of hobnail boots! The air of the beach was fouled by strong language. A soft spot Jack might have for the poor bloody infantry; a sympathy, an understanding, a love of his brothers-in-arms and a compassion which transcended watery bounds, but he did not have the slightest desire to emulate the bloody 'squaddy' and said so in no uncertain terms. But emulate him he did. Mustered there upon the beach in orderly ranks the sailors were loud and bitter in condemnation of all things military and, to a man, threatened to 'slap in ta see sum bastard about this bloody skylark' and merciless in its intensity, the sun beat down from the unfeeling heavens.

'Right, my lads!' bawled a Captain from a Royal Marines Commando, bronzed, fit and disgustingly athletic-looking who was in charge of the training. 'Your ship has been hit by gunfire from an enemy shore battery.' 'Hard shit!' said Jack. 'And you are on the beach and Jerry is just over the way.' He waved a vague hand in the general direction of the unfriendly desert.

'Follow me!' he roared; so saying and with the typical sweeping, over-arm gesture which brooked no disinclination, he went galloping up the beach, as someone in the ranks said, 'like a bleedin' pukka dink majah 'oppin' ovah the poxy top!' Any reluctance on the part of the peasantry to follow him was soon scotched by the proddings of a Colour Sergeant, Royal Marines, whose sole purpose in life was to see that there were no shirkers in the ranks. 'Such language – an' 'im a Colour Sergeant too!' With long loping strides the Captain led the way up the beach and over the road which hugs the North African coast from Alexandria to Algiers, built by the Romans the Professor said in between puffing and wiping the sand out of his eyes. 'Built by Scipio Africanus,' he gasped. 'Fuck is luck,' said 'Shiner' Wright, Able Seaman from the City of Exeter. After the first quarter of a mile Jack was flaked out; another quarter of the same and he was down to his ankle bones. But the officer in charge was not to be deterred from his purpose; amphibious warfare was his business and amphibious warfare he would have. He encouraged, he wheedled, he insulted and he swore most atrociously in his efforts to keep them moving – where and for what purpose no one knew, or cared.

'Scatter, men – keep yer 'eads down – attack, attack, attack – fire, fire, fire!' 'Lucky fer 'im we ain't got no ammynishun 'relse 'ee'd uv 'ad 'is fuckin' bloody 'ead blowed orf – the man's a bleedin' 'ead case!'

With the sun at its zenith he goaded the sailors beyond nautical endurance and pushed them nigh unto death; indeed death in the desert would have been a merciful release from the hands of this madman and from the labours of the day. On the march back to the ship and to the promised swim he added insult to injury by exhorting everyone to sing. The brigade of cripples and walking wounded treated their tormentor to a stony silence and a withering contempt. He was furious.

'C'mon' he bawled, 'Sing, you bastards, sing!' So they dutifully sang:

'They were fuckin' in the hallway,
Fuckin' on the stairs,
Yew couldn't see the carpet
Fer the cunt an' curly 'airs.
Singin' ro-tiddly O, shit or bust,
Never let yer bollocks dangle in the dust.'

Never had the 'Ball of Kirriemuir' been rendered with such lack of spirit. The contingent wended its weary way back to the ship, crawled over the ramp, staggered down to the messdecks and there died a thousand deaths. Bugger the swim! – and for days thereafter hobbled around in gym shoes.

If the Good Lord in His Wisdom had meant sailors to be soldiers He would have made them with built-in hobnail boots: 't'ain't nacheral all this 'ere bloody 'oofin' about. The furthest I wants to march in future is from the dockyard gates to the nearest boozer!' So were expressed the sentiments of all concerned, and as if to emphasize these sentiments, all went ashore in a body after the blisters had healed, and adjourned to the 'Pig and Whistle' in Alexandria where, as it was expressed after a monumental run ashore, they got as pissed as newts. Never had pints of 'icers' tasted so good; the makeshift commandos quaffed the stuff by the gallon and boasted to the world at large of their prowess 'on the hoof'. 'God 'elp Jerry if we've ever gotta go ashore!' They then returned to their ship in a fleet of feluccas to the haunting refrain of 'The Matelot's Lament':

'Side, side LST's side,
The Jimmy looks on 'er wiv pride,
' 'ee'd frow a pink fit

If 'e saw all the shit
Down there on LST's side.
Roll out the *Nelson*, the *Rodney*, *Renown*,
This flat-bottomed bastard is gettin' me down.'

From Alexandria the ship without a name, she had a number, ran through the Suez Canal to Port Tewfik at the canal's southern extremity for more exercises; and the tedium of waiting for God only knew what was alleviated by further runs ashore in new territory. Tewfik itself had little to offer, and everyone walked the two miles along the causeway to mainland Port Suez. The greater part of the town was off limits; so it was there that the Professor and Johnny Thomas, and a few randomly chosen shipmates went and experienced a very strange adventure.

But before attempting the long and exhausting walk along the hot and dusty causeway, they repaired to a local hostelry, 'The First and Last', and there drank in preparation for the pedestrian ordeal which lay ahead. Inside the bar it was refreshingly cool and the beer was ice-cold East African lager from Dar es Salaam, a passable brew; everyone relaxed and settled down to enjoy the drink. But not for long were they to be left in peace; that was not in the nature of things Arabic and there entered a shifty looking gentleman dressed in European clothes and carrying quite the biggest camera on legs that any of the party had ever seen; vintage 1900, or thereabouts, and complete with black and voluminous 'hideaway' hood.

'Photeegraaaf, maaasters – photeegraaaf.'

The photographs, not being of the pornographic variety, aroused little interest. 'Imshi, yalla!'

'Photeegraaaf,' he grinned, he whined and the assembled company refused; they were adamant in their expressed wish not to be photographed, even if his name was Achmed bin Abdullah ben Hakim who claimed to be the 'best, bloody, goddamned, alright, cor blimey, don't give me the shits, Jack, photeegraaaf man in all Egypt.' After the self-adulation he grinned the more and he whined the more; apart from being the best photographer in Egypt, he was, strangely enough, also a starving photographer who had sixteen starving kids and four insatiable wives to maintain. 'Justa smallee photeegraaaf. Up ol' Farouk's fat ass, Jack!'

The party succumbed. Why not? A little souvenir of the run ashore, the group to include two coal black soldiers of the King's African Rifles, who grinning all over their faces, had been watching the scene. The Professor and 'Smelly' Feates Stoker 1st Class, swapped hats with the soldiers; with big looks and cheesy smiles the party formed up to 'watchee birdee'.

With arms waving adjustments to the posing group the photographer disappeared under the folds of his voluminous hood; his fat backside protruded like the stern sheets of a rhinoceros backing out of a bush and his muffled voice waffled away in Arabic. With the Professor and 'Smelly' wearing bush hats with snakeskin bands the group 'watcheeed' the 'birdeee' and after what seemed an age the job was done and the photogenic tipplers returned to the more serious business of the day scuppering 'icers'. Meanwhile the photographer dived into a mysterious black box and with an enamel bucket threatened to ' 'velup um, preteee damn quick all right.'

This he did, and asked an extortionate price for the results of his labours. 'Sheer, bleedin' daylight robbery! – Imshi, yalla!' And in a matelot's words they told him precisely what he could do with his photographs. Argument raged and for once an Arab gentleman of commerce refused to drop his price; he became annoyed and demanded his rightful dues, but the party were already in possession of the prints which had been passed around for their approval; a scuffle ensued as the irate owner tried to snatch back his property. Someone, it sounded like 'Cuts' Curtis, Leading Stoker, shouted: 'Fit 'is bleedin' camera over 'is 'ead!'

No sooner said than done, and the luckless photographer reeled around the bar hoodwinked and blind, his head encased in the box of his camera, and with the legs sticking out in front for all the world like a triple-horned minotaur; from inside the box were heard Arabic imprecations. By the time he had removed the offending box from his skull the disputants had fled hotfoot up the causeway and almost incoherent with laughter. But as they slowed to a walk and glanced over their shoulders, the laughter died in their throats; for there pounding up the road in hot pursuit was the irate cameraman, and in his wake a whole posse of his ilk, white-robed and tarbooshed, all earnest and threatening in the heat of the noonday sun. Fists were being waved and there came the glint of naked steel brandished high; the sailors, hilarity flown, took to their heels in deadly earnest. Desperation gifted their heels with wings and they beat the photographer and his henchmen to the comparative safety of the streets of Port Suez by a clear two hundred yards. In no time at all the sailors got lost amongst the teeming crowds of the alleyways and bazaars and by some strange mischance found themselves near a bar, which was secluded, and proclaimed to the world that it sold ice-cold beer; the hunted went to earth.

Beer all round was the order; mine host shuffled around with bottles and glasses and consternation reigned in his establishment; his customers were thunder-struck; out of the six of them only one had a wallet, paybook or loose change to his name. They had been robbed!

Philosophical acceptance of the vagaries of fate was ever the matelot's strength; they quaffed their ale and soon began to laugh anew at the antics of the hard-done-by photographer. They still had the prints which were passed around for perusal; the sallies and the wit were kept up until their attention was attracted by a 'gully gully' man who, equipped with his box of tricks, had just entered the bar.

'Gully gully,' he croaked in Canal Zone English, 'Gully gully – yew laak gully gully?' Whether they liked it or not, they got it and the itinerant magician was soon pulling all his tricks out of a repertoire that was as old as the pyramids; old indeed before Moses cast his staff before the Lord in Midian. But this time there was a difference; the gully gully man seemed to crave a greater intimacy; 'Perish the thought, an' 'im such a dirty bastard too!' He leaned over the Professor and in perfect English hissed in his ear: 'Pay no attention to me. When I have finished feel your hip pocket, but on no account let on that anything out of the ordinary has happened.'

Amazed, he did as he was bidden; he felt his pocket and there to his further amazement was his wallet and paybook which upon later examination proved to contain his money still. He could hardly conceal his incredulity and, had it not been for further warning hisses from gully gully man, would not have done so. That gentleman continued his performance and, one after the other, the same thing happened to the rest of the party. Finally, smiling and deeply bowing, the gully gully man backed out of the door after having first collected his baksheesh and disappeared into the crowded alley.

' 'oo'd yew reckon 'e wus, Prof?'

'Christ knows – search me.'

'Reckon 'e mustabin a British agent er sumfin?'

'Reckon 'e mustabin, – 'oo else would 'ave done a thing like that?'

Keeping a weather eye cocked for the owner of the late and obviously much lamented camera the party threaded their way through the labyrinth of the town and headed back to their ship. As they neared the start of the causeway and light was beginning to fade, a figure appeared from out of the shadow of a wall. On closer inspection the figure revealed itself as a dirty old Arab in evil-smelling robes.

In the tray suspended from his neck by a piece of string he carried the usual assortment of junk: tin bracelets, worthless coins, beads, Egyptian matches – every one guaranteed to light, – contraceptives, and Spanish Fly in little, brown bottles.

'Yew buy Spaneesh Fly, maasters – plenty jiggee jig.'

It was their considered opinion that Spanish Fly did not work; it was only coloured water. They also told him to piss off, sharpish, or, perhaps, a little sooner. Then, to their surprise, he said, in the native tongue of his listeners: 'I should have handed those paybooks in you know.'

They goggled anew, and the Professor was the first to find his voice: 'Yew!' he exclaimed. 'Yew – How did yew find them anyway?'

'Your mate the photographer.' The dirty old Arab chuckled. 'You fitted him up fair and square – did us a favour there – but I won't go into details – lucky for you we had our eye on him – on your way, be good, and don't do any of the things I do. Cheerio, chaps.' And off he went limping down the causeway.

'Well I'm buggered – Did yew ever see the likes o' that?' John Thomas spoke for them all.

'One thing's fer sure,' 'Smelly' said; 'I'll never kick a wog's ass again – never know 'oo yew might be kickin'!'

They were supposed to be back inside the dockyard gates before dark; it was by now well after the hour of curfew for the sailors, but they ambled back; it did not really matter; no one would worry too much; a funny old Navy was the LSTs.

Training intensified and necessitated a trip to the southern end of the Red Sea, to Djibouti in French Somaliland, to pick up a contingent of Senegalese troops for transport to Algiers. Except for their officers who were white, bitter and twisted Frenchmen, these troops were, as someone said, 'as black as the 'obs uv 'ell.' They were a dirty, smelly and servile crowd and were on their way home to Senegal via Algiers. Getting to Algiers through the Sicilian Narrows presented no problem; nothing was seen of the *Luftwaffe* or the E-Boats and U-Boats. The shooting war in North Africa was over.

Algiers, city of romance, contrast and French imperialism; a city of wealth and privilege contrasted with abject poverty; a city where necessity was a vice and vice was a necessity and a thriving industry; here was every shade of skin from white to black. A city of grand, spacious, tree-lined boulevards and avenues adorned with statues of the notables of France and her colonies; here stood plush hotels, multiple stores and luxury apartments. Here was a kasbah, dark alleys and the hovels of the native poor whence daily at dawn emerged beggars, thieves, pimps and prostitutes. There were, of course, those who emerged to earn an honest living, but such were hard to find in the Algiers which saw the flight of Rommel's army. From El-Biar where all the best people lived, down to the Sahel Door, the gateway to the old fortress city that was the kasbah, Algiers was a beautiful city. But once through the Sahel Door the centuries were rolled back and the days of the notorious piratical pashas were reborn. Even the reedy music of the pipes and the thin and plaintive wail of the song which emanated from dark doorways was reminiscent of another age; an age of corsair, blackamoor, and Mozarab. Everywhere there was an air of mystery, a sense of corruption and low life; an all-pervading smell of danger, romance and high adventure hung over the ancient city of the Caliphate. The place, of course, was out of bounds to all service personnel.

From this place of degradation emerged the Professor, Johnny Thomas and two other shipmates of an adventurous turn of mind. They came out quite openly through the Sahel Door, passed the barbed wire and the Military Police, to follow their guide and mentor around the corner, down a side street and into a small, dark and evil-smelling wine shop where they breathed a sigh of relief and threw off their all-concealing white robes.

From Algiers they went to Tripoli, once more to load troops; but this time they were British troops, men of the Guard's Armoured Brigade, the elite; and something, it appeared, was about to happen. Rumour was rife; this was the real thing – invasion. But where?

The ships sailed in glorious weather, and with them they took the tanks, troops and all the paraphernalia of war. Everyone was briefed in transit, it was to be Sicily, the invasion of Europe was on at last. The weather deteriorated, the sea was whipped up by an exacting, nor'westerly wind, and the sky grew ugly; all was not well with the invasion fleet. The soldiery spewed, lay down and wished to die; tanks broke loose and careered about the decks of the rolling ships; and on the treacherously slippery steel decks, soldiers and sailors took their lives in their hands as they fought to resecure the cumbersome steel monsters. It was not a happy time.

Dawn broke over another day, and there ahead of the ships was Sicily; the weather improved and anxious eyes strained towards the shore. Engine-room telegraphs rang down for more speed; then the ships slowed and rammed hard on to the enemy shore; bow doors opened, ramps went down, and off into the beautiful land of Sicily roared the agents of retribution: tanks, guns, armoured cars, jeeps, lorries, troops and ambulances.

Accompanied by the harsh screeching of tank tracks, the roaring of revving engines and the skirl of a lone Highlander's pipes, the soldiers went into battle. Guns belched smoke, flame, shot and defiance at the enemy, and into the morning the battle raged; into the morning and on until high noon, and the sound of its raging did not lessen. Things were not going well. The beachhead was gained and a foothold was being held, but the enemy was firmly entrenched in the hills to the north of Noto, west of the Avola beachhead. The British monitor *Erebus* turned her huge 16-inch guns on the area and, supported by cruisers and destroyers, began a methodical clean up. The noise of the bombardment was deafening; the flash and roar of the guns, the whining and soughing of the shells and the 'crump-crump' of their explosion turned that Sicilian day into a hell upon earth, a man-made holocaust; over all hung a pall of dust and cordite smoke, and the smell of men's stupidity fouled the air of this 'the fairest garden of the Mediterranean'.

Now that the troops were ashore there was little that could be done in the Tank Landing Ships except 'fight ship' when the enemy bombers came and wait for such little tide as there was to come in and float them off the beach.

These nameless ships, the LSTs, were a strange Navy; a Navy where everyone did very much as they pleased, dressed as they pleased and, within reason, came and went as they pleased. It was almost a private Navy. It was officered by men of the Royal Naval Reserve from the Merchant Navy, and by men of the Royal Naval Volunteer Reserve, 'bloody Saturday Night Sailors' or by wartime sailors who had been given a commission and who wore wavy rings on their sleeves the same as did the RNVR types; there was little discipline as the 'proper RN' knew it and any resemblance to the parent body was purely accidental. This happy state of affairs came about because this admirable body of men did not know or particularly like the rules for the conduct of naval affairs as laid down by Their Lordships of Admiralty. It was truthfully said by 'John of' or 'Gormless' Gaunt, Chief of all the Torpedo Gunners' Mates, the 'swine' (Coxswain) of the Professor's ship, that 'Jimmy the One' as just retribution for misdemeanour's, ' 'Ould jest as soon chin ya as troop ya,' (Punch one on the chin rather than place one on the Captain's Report); the hands were as likely to be called in the morning by the toe of the First Lieutenant's boot as they were by the trilling of the Bosun's Call. The First Lieutenant was a 'rum un'; he had spent most of his working life running tramp steamers up and down the China coast, and spoke Cantonese with greater fluency than he spoke his native tongue. The Captain was heir to a chain of multiple stores and had spent a lot of his life learning his seamanship by driving the family yacht, which was rumoured to be as big as a destroyer; both of them saw defaulters but rarely. 'Rig of the Day' at sea or in harbour was khaki shorts and 'pusser's crabs' (boots), without socks and laces; if on watch the men wore bathing trunks and lanyards; the latter were worn around the neck with a 'pusser's dirk' (combination knife and marlin spike) dangling from the end. To say that there was no discipline would not be true; the men who served these strange ships implemented their own brand of discipline, a discipline which owed more to loyalty to the 'old man' and the ship than it did to King's Regulations and Admiralty Instructions. Any self-respecting Master-at-Arms would have thrown a pink fit as soon as he stepped on board, but the ships for landing tanks did not carry such exalted citizens; and even without 'Jossmen' (Masters-at-Arms) these ships did a wonderful, if sometimes rather piratical, job of work.

It was inevitable that such ships, employed on such duties, should carry stores – masses of them. Such stores were legitimate 'perks' for the pilfering sailor; indeed they were carried, it would seem, for his special benefit as a dispensation to lower deck *laissez-faire*. For instance there was the occasion when fifty cases of canned beer were spirited away from the jetty in Algiers and, to the lasting chagrin of the NAAFI Manager, not a single case nor as much as an empty can ever turned up to show where the spirit had removed them. There was another occasion when half a ton of corned beef was 'mislaid' in Syracuse; through the philanthropic agency of Jack the starving urchins of that ancient seat of learning prospered and waxed fat on the stuff for weeks thereafter.

Later the ships were to carry American troops and American stores; Jack and half the population of Syracuse, Catania and Palermo walked around smoking big, fat cigars, and passed round Chesterfields, Lucky Strikes, Camels and chewing gum with all the open-handed philanthropy of 'GI Joes'. The sailors also took to wearing best tailored American infantry denims and windcheaters with nudes painted on the back; windcheaters which also had painted upon them such cheerful legends as 'She's my Gal', 'Lulu', 'Lucky 'Frisco', 'The Yellow Rose of Texas' and 'Wait 'till Johnny Comes Marching Home'. A stranger boarding the LSTs might have imagined himself anywhere from Fort Worth to Pawtucket Field; anywhere but in one of His Britannic Majesty's Ships of War.

The matelots of the LSTs were incorrigible and veritable 'Robin Hoods'; they robbed the rich and the mighty to feed the poor and the infirm; the starving populace of the Sicilian seaboard fed on American turkey and ham, British corned beef, baked beans and canned 'bangers'. Many a war-shattered Italian brat had Jack to thank for the first square meal he or she had eaten in years, or the only pair of boots that they had ever possessed, even though American Government Issue, 'infantry for the use of' and six sizes too big, but a pair of boots to display proudly on the streets to envious friends nevertheless. Nothing was sacred from these seagoing, light-fingered gentry, 'robbin' bastards' some said they were; but to their lasting credit few of them ever made a penny from their trade. A bottle or two of Marsala maybe, a basket of fruit perhaps, a night or possibly an afternoon spent in bed with the urchin's grateful mother or sister, but nothing more. Jack's needs were very simple and utterly fundamental; he was not out to line his pocket; money had no value anyway, but he did a power of good for his soul and perhaps he spread a little happiness in this most unhappy land.

Such was the manner in which the unconventional men who served these unconventional ships spread abroad the goodwill of the Allied cause; and it was this, the spirit of the LSTs, which took Jack ashore on that dramatic morning of the Sicilian 'D-Day'. The troops and armour had barely cleared the beach, the tide would not be back for another twelve hours, so there was time for a 'shopping run', a mooch ashore to find out 'wot might be loafin''; in khaki shorts, laceless boots, without socks, with a pocketful of French letters, and wearing his tin hat, the Professor joined forces with some six or so of his intrepid shipmates and the whole party was led by that redoubtable moocher, the granddaddy of all the 'infiltrators', and 'fiddler-in-chief', Leading Seaman Michael Seamus Joseph Patrick O'Dougherty, from

Dublin. Before the Royal Navy had claimed Mick's allegiance he had been a gravedigger, as had his father and his father's father before him; he claimed, that between them they had buried every member of the Irish Republican Army who had ever 'snuffed it'. That morning he came very close to digging his own grave and nearly failed to return to his peacetime profession, and his hobby of fighting the English. With the party was a soldier, a veteran of the Western Desert, who was attached to the Army Liaison Unit aboard the ship.

'Don't go in there!' He screamed the warning.

Arm raised, about to push open the door in front of him, Mick paused; that pause saved his life and those of his shipmates who were with him.

'Don't fer gawd's sake touch it,' the soldier warned again; he fetched a large stone from a nearby wall and shouting to everyone to take cover, heaved it at the door and dived for cover himself. The door of the large barn-like building swung slowly on its hinges and suddenly the door and half the front wall were blown out by a sharp explosion. The soldier picked himself up and gazed ruefully at the pile of shattered masonry and slowly settling dust; the others, white and shaken, emerged from behind their protective wall.

The soldier went forward and peered into the building; he heaved more stones and after a thorough inspection pronounced himself satisfied. It was safe to enter and slowly and timorously the others crowded in, gaining in confidence as they watched the soldier walking around and peering about; no more booby traps, he said, and they took his word for it. He should know; he had come through the desert unscathed.

The large building which they had entered proved to be the vat house of a vineyard; four huge maturing vats lined the walls; looking like oversized barrels, they measured some fifteen feet in diameter.

'Phwat's that!' Mick was intrigued.

'Wine.' The Professor tapped the vat. 'Vino – Marsala or somethin'.'

'Be the Holy Mhither uv Jaysus – ar' ya tellin' me dat dat's all bhooze?'

Mick was incredulous; he reckoned that there was enough booze there to swim in, let alone take a bath in, and with his huge shovel-splayed hands he tried to turn on the taps, but they would not budge; he looked for a spanner, but as there was no spanner to be found, he kicked the offending taps; then, putting his hand into the back pocket of his shorts, he pulled out a German Luger automatic pistol for which he had paid a thirst-crazed GI a bottle of neat rum, and, telling everyone to stand back, shot two neat holes in the vat, one at the bottom and one at the top to let the air in, and a thin red stream of wine ran out.

'Vino!' he exclaimed, and vino it was, and drinkable – thousands of gallons of the stuff. More holes were shot in more vats; seven thirsty throats applied themselves to seven wine-streaming holes, and six sailors and one soldier rolled back on board their ship, arms linked in good fellowship, singing and impervious to the crash of guns and whining shells; drunk as an Admiral's flunkeys they were and back in the vat house gallons of rich red wine flowed to enrich the Sicilian soil.

During the days which followed there was fierce opposition from the enemy shore batteries; but as the days progressed the opposition was battered into submission and the noise of the battle receded from the beaches. The dreaded *Luftwaffe* flew near from time to time, but they did not like the quality or the quantity of the opposition and were beaten off. The only success they could claim with any degree of certainty was the sinking of a hospital ship which, laden with wounded and with red crosses as big as double-decker buses painted on her side and upper works, was soon reduced to a shambles of blazing wreckage and screaming men before she rolled over and sank. The tide, such as there was, would not refloat the beached LSTs and, after trying the tides over three days, they were towed off by destroyers. From the beaches they returned to Tripoli for more troops, tanks and guns; from Tripoli to Syracuse and Augusta and back to Bizerta; from Bizerta to Catania and back to Philippeville; from Philippeville to Taormina and back to Oran; from Oran to Palermo and back to Malta; and so it went on, day after day, load after load, working the clock around until everyone was fit to drop from exhaustion; then one day there were no more Germans and Italians left in Sicily and no more fighting on the island. The day was won and the British were masters in the Mediterranean.

The sailors ranged far and wide; from Catania to have a look at Mount Etna; from Taormina to a place called Linguaglossa on the volcano's northern slopes; it was here at Bronte that Lord Nelson derived one of his titles, so they were keeping the very best of company; and to Francavilla and Mandanici; from Palermo to Monreale, Bagheria, Piana and Mondello; anywhere that could produce a bottle of wine, and where the signorinas were partial to chocolate and cigarettes.

This former enemy accepted the men of the invading forces with a philosophical shrug; to these depressed, impoverished inhabitants of Italy's degraded south one master was as good as another; the Nazi, the Fascisti, the British, the Americanos, the Mafia, what did it matter? They had not wanted the war anyway, and with the invaders there had come a new, if temporary, prosperity; people could eat again, and that to people who measured their loyalties in terms of calories per day was all that really mattered. Money had no value; paper and coin were worthless; food was what people craved; food and the basic necessities of life, and for these they prostituted their bodies and sold their souls.

There came another dawn and the Landing Ships (Tanks) crossed the Straits of Messina; for the first time since June, 1940, British troops stood on the mainland of Europe; before them via Naples, Rome, Genoa and Paris lay the road to Berlin. Mussolini had decamped; the Italian Government had disintegrated; everywhere was chaos and Italy was on the verge of surrender. It was a time of great rejoicing in the British ships; the threat of the Italian Navy was gone for ever and it seemed that the *Luftwaffe* had lost interest. On the beaches of Calabria the Italians surrendered in their tens of thousands; they threw down their guns, accepted cigarettes and were issued with shovels to dig out the bogged-down tanks which emerged from the bowels of the ships to invade their homeland; and as they dug they sang, grinned and were grateful to be captured; grateful for the food, grateful for the cigarettes and above all grateful that for them the war was over.

After Messina and Reggio came Salerno which was further north again; there was talk about 'working a flanker', namely getting behind the enemy lines, cutting him off and thus shortening the war. American troops this time and, of course, American stores; the Professor's ship was honoured by the presence on passage to the beaches of a top American General and his staff. All very top brass, frightfully important, zero hour stuff; after the troops had been ashore for five days the General sent his Chief of Staff back to the ship to fetch the maps and operational plans which the General had forgotten and which, after a frantic search, were found in a large leather folio case behind the Wardroom settee.

In his usual position in the starboard wing of the upper bridge the Professor stood and, as did everyone else, strained his eyes into the shrouding darkness of just before the dawn to where, a few miles ahead, the beaches of Salerno lay silent and full of menace. Over this scene the heavy air of pre-action expectancy hung like a muffling shroud; a stifling cloud of tension emanated from the men about to go into battle; every man was silent with his thoughts and his fear. This time things would be different and tougher; there would be no spineless Italians to oppose this landing; the 'Eyeties' were out of the war; this time the assault was to be behind the German lines and Intelligence had intimated that the enemy was waiting. In the coastal hills beyond the beaches a crack Panzer division lurked; at any moment might come the spiteful whap-whap of their 88mm guns; the tracer could come burning out of the dawn or the divebombers scream out of the lightening sky.

These were the things the men in the ships, sailors and soldiers alike, feared; in their hearts was a dread of the coming day. The invasion fleet had already been attacked by the *Luftwaffe,* and there was a fear abroad that this presaged a resurgence of the old spirit of the *Fliegerkorps.*

The Professor strained his eyes to where the beaches lay and thought of the dawn; yet another dawn and he was sick to death of dawns – there had been too many dawns. And he was afraid, afraid that one of these dawns might prove to be his last.

Behind him in the darkness figures moved; subdued voices as the Captain spoke down the voicepipe to the helmsman; or the Yeoman of Signals repeated a message from the Radio Room where the Telegraphist was tuned in to the Officer Commanding the assault forces; mingled with the normal sounds of the bridge the Professor could hear the lazy American drawl of the General's Staff, when there came to his ears a voice he knew, a voice a little louder and more insistent, a voice with a note of outrage, the voice of the Captain's Steward. The Steward was always on the bridge at sea; the Captain had decreed that it be so and to the lasting disgust of the Yeoman of Signals he slung his hammock athwart the flag deck with a highhandedness and a Captain-sponsored impunity over which the Yeoman had no jurisdiction.

'Hey, mush – that's my mick yew'm kipped in!'

No response, and again the voice of the Steward: 'Hey, hey – 'eave o' 'eave o' – 'op out afore I pulls yew out!'

A small silence, then the voice of the American General: 'Huh, a-a-a-aw – jest a-settin' heah – jest a-settin' – Musta dozed off I guess – Yeah shore, son, mightee sawry boy – yew all hittin' the sack!'

'Jacky' Dawes had no intention of 'hittin' the sack' on such an auspicious occasion as the invasion of Salerno; he was at action stations like everyone else; he had merely come to lash up his hammock before all hell broke loose and the 'mick' got in the way of 'fighting ship'; besides, he wanted his American-issue wind-cheater as protection against the early chill.

'Sorry, Sir – Oh no, Sir – jest lookin' fer summat, Sir.' 'Jacky' fussed and nearly bent over backwards in his attempts to placate the General, but he need not have bothered. 'Sir' needed no soothing; he merely chuckled deeply and said: 'OK son – she's all yourn.'

The Professor laughed silently at poor Jacky's words. That must have been the first time ever an American General or any other General had been threatened with a dumping on the deck beneath a 'pusser's mick.'

Suddenly and with a fearful scraping noise the Landing Ships (Tanks) grounded on the beach at Salerno and all hell broke loose. Everyone's worst fears were soon realized; the Germans were there in strength and the tanks and infantry fought hard for every yard of beach; glowing skeins of tracer came streaming out from the shore to rattle like hailstones on a tin roof against the sides of the assaulting craft. There came the vicious whap of the German heavy artillery and the guns of the Tiger tanks; the shells droned and soughed and threw up columns of sand in front of the grounding ships. The anti-tank guns, accompanied by the spine-chilling judder of machine guns, exacted a heavy toll and the whole beach erupted into a battleground of shot, sand and desperate endeavour.

In the ships, as on all such occasions, there was little that could be done to assist the land battle. They had delivered the troops to their landfall and now they must sit back and wait for the returning tide to refloat them. Such armament as the assault craft possessed was of little use in this kind of fight; ships were never designed to fight tanks at close range. From seaward there was no supporting bombardment from the big ships; there were no big ships; they were all on the northern, British sector; the Yanks, it was said, had refused to land under a naval bombardment.

Full daylight found the land battle raging fiercely, not three hundred yards from the ships. The tide had receded leaving the LSTs high and dry, sitting on their flat bottoms like a long line of broody ducks – sitting ducks for the artillery and the Tiger tanks – with the sea, their natural habitat and their *raison d'être,* half a mile astern. Not a healthy situation. There were German tanks between them and the sea; and that day the LSTs laid claim to being the first ships of the Royal Navy or any other Navy ever to take part in a tank battle.

The Tiger tanks of the Panzer unit, black and sinister and with black and white crosses painted on their swivelling gun turrets, raced along the beach belching death and destruction at the khaki-coloured tanks with the white stars on their sides; the khaki tanks chased them back again, keeping them preoccupied and away from those precious ships; if all did not go according to plan, those ships were the troops' back door.

'Good ol' tanks. Shoot the black bastards. Oh, my Christ! That was close – duck! Good ol' Yank. Got the bastard! Watch it, matey! Turn round, yew stupid fucker! Rotten luck!' Jack was a spectator in the bows of the ships; he ducked when the shot and debris came too close and hurled advice and abuse at the contestants; it was the only form of assistance he had to offer at that moment. A shell from a German tank-mounted 88mm gun, or it might have come from a Yankee 75 pounder, hit the Professor's ship fair and square, well above the water line on the port side, screamed through the messdecks at waist height and exited via the bulkhead on the starboard side. In transit it failed to hit anything or anybody, and the only record of its passing were two neat holes in the ship's sides, one to port and one to starboard, and 'Jack Dusty's' dhobi-ing got scorched.

At the northern end of the beach was an American LST which, being the first in line, bore the brunt of the artillery fire. The number of holes shot through her plating reached astronomic proportions; she was christened 'USS *Pepperpot*' and certain it was that she would never leave the scene of her transient glory.

For five bitter and bloody days and nights the battle raged back and forth, and neither side lost or gained the ground of the original beachhead. It was a military stalemate and Winston Churchill broadcast a sombre message to the nation; a message which presaged a possible withdrawal from Salerno. But it did not happen; the LSTs were eventually pulled off the beaches and back to Tripoli, Oran and Philippeville; to Bougie, Algiers and Malta they went for reinforcements. These were thrown into the fray and the offensive intensified; there was rumour of disaffection in high places; the Trans-Atlantic *entente cordiale* was not, apparently, working very well, and such a rumour did not encourage affection amongst the men who fought the battles. The renewed assault was met with fierce opposition and a forceful counter-attack; again the battle raged upon the beaches which, for the second time, were almost lost to the enemy.

Jack's plaint was loud and bitter, his condemnation of American mismanagement caustic and his criticism sharply barbed. To the Prime Minister's Sunday morning speech he listened with grave face and a sickening stomach. 'That's us 'e's talkin' about – that's our bloody battle!' More reserves were sent in, this time stiffened with British armour; a heavy bombardment was agreed and duly mounted; and slowly the noises of battle receded to the north through the gap in the coastal hills and out upon the road to Naples and Rome.

After the first withdrawal from the beach, in the time of indecision and uncertainty, the LSTs lay offshore and the Professor and his shipmates stood on deck, almost under the guns of the mighty *Warspite, Rodney* and *Nelson,* and watched the monsters bombard the shore. It was so close to hand and a tremendous thing to see. 'Bong' would go the firing circuits as pre-firing tests were made; then there was a heavy, interminable moment of suspense until a mighty flash licked out from the huge gun barrels, followed – it seemed an age later – by the roar of the broadside; into the shore, whining and soughing like a swiftly diminishing wind, went the shells. A few moments later there came the rushings and the soughings of enemy shells coming in the opposite direction; but the Germans gunners might as well have shot peas at a brick wall; the battleships were invulnerable, or were until a 'Chase-me-Charlie' glider bomb hit *Warspite* and the belligerent old lady was forced to retire from the fray.

At some time during the action, hangdog and tails down, the Italian fleet steamed by. To the Professor, Johnny Thomas, and the others present who had known the bitterness and horror of the war's early days in these waters, the sight was a revelation. Perhaps the escorting men o' war from the Royal Navy brought these ships close in to the invasion fleet purposely to hearten the sailors. If so, they certainly achieved their purpose, and men wondered how such fine ships had proved such ineffective instruments of war. Great powerful battleships – modern, potent and bristling with guns. Sleek, racy cruisers and destroyers – superior to anything possessed by the Mediterranean Fleet which had faced them in the dark days of Greece, Crete and the Malta convoys. Now they steamed to the south, ironically, to internment at Malta. This was the British Navy's first real close-up look at the ships which had opposed them, all of which were said to be capable of the most fantastic speeds; all previous sightings had been from astern. These were the ships which should have done battle with obsolete battleships, old cruisers and a pitifully inadequate number of hard-pressed and run-to-death destroyers. These were the 'long distance runners' of Matapan and Spartivento; with resolution on their bridges and courage between their decks, these ships could have changed the history of the world.

After Salerno came Anzio and another attempt to get behind the enemy and shorten the war. Here also things were not good. Here also the invading forces felt the pronged fork of stiffening resistance.

'Knock-knock' Naylor was cut in half by a German shell; the Professor stared horrified at the kicking torsoless legs of his number two on the gun as they went running down the deck before collapsing in a tangle, and he vomited into what was left of 'Knock-knock's' belly. Anzio was nearer to the enemy's airfields in northern Italy; the bombers had not so far to fly and they made a horror of the days and a living hell of the nights.

On the way back to Naples for reinforcements the men of the LSTs could hear the rumble of the guns as the battles were fought on the coastal road which hugged the Tyrrhenian Sea from Reggio in the south to San Remo in the north; the road which ran via Capua and Cassino to Rome.

In Naples, which had now fallen to the Allies, the sailors heard of Monte Cassino, a monastery founded, so it was said, by Saint Benedict himself; home of art treasures and the culture of the ages, a house of God on top of a mountain. 'Benedictine – Wasn't that the name uv some sort uv booze wot all the nobs drink? Booze er not, whacker, the place is takin' a right pasting, so they sez' and, on the next trip up to Anzio, just as dawn was breaking, they saw the Allied bombers go in over the mountains and heard the artillery rumbling in the valleys around Mignano and Pontecorvo. It was said that the Germans were using the monastery as an advanced headquarters. 'Bit rough on them poor bleedin' monks!' The mountain erupted and much that was old and beautiful was reduced to rubble; part of man's heritage perished in the dawn and the ships sailed on to Anzio.

As if the guns, the bombers and all the other horrors attendant upon the successful prosecution of war were not enough, Vesuvius erupted and dealt itself a hand in the game of destruction.

The LSTs were lying in the Gulf of Naples at Castellammare di Stabia, a few miles north of Sorrento and Capri which enhance the Gulf's southern shore. The sky above the volcano had for many nights been lit by the glow cast up from the earth's uneasy bowels; the glow grew more bright, the earth rumbled with increasing menace and the pungent smell of sulphur was in the air. Just such a prelude, nearly two thousand years before, had warned of the engulfment of Pompeii and Herculaneum and, as then, the eruption came in the night. The rumblings grew louder, the glow at the cone glowed more bright and suddenly the night sky was illuminated by a greater glow which flickered momentarily around the heavens and then died away; again there was a great light and a momentary flickering in the sky; molten lava was hurled high into the air and fell like glowing rain on to the mountain's steep, sloping sides. Down from the glowing cone, incandescent in the darkness, ran streams of molten lava; and down upon the men watching fascinated from the decks of the ships there showered a light rain of sulphurous lava dust. The eruption was not serious, but it served to illustrate the puniness of the machinations of men at war and, perhaps, as some said, to betoken Divine displeasure.

Naples basked in the autumn sunshine, and in the gaze of the sailors from the LSTs who, for the most part, were seeing the city for the first time. Naples, romantic city of song, gaiety and legend. Here, from the Roman Emperors to the Victorians, had come famous men, seeking inspiration, relaxation and escape. Here Lord Nelson had fallen in love. Perhaps the seekers of the past had found the things for which they sought; the sailors from the invasion fleet did not; they found a drab, battle-scarred city of destruction and human misery.

Naples was ever the scene of poverty and human degradation; but now, as the German armies retreated to the north, the city's shame and debasement reached an all-time low. Searching through the rubble of their shattered city to find something to barter for food the people starved; if they found nothing to barter, they bartered their wives, their daughters and even their sons. Women and girls sold themselves in the streets, infant pimps roamed the city soliciting on behalf of mothers and sisters; the only price they asked for their degradation was food. For food they sold their souls and committed every crime, from picking pockets to murder. Gangs of children roamed the streets, often armed with knives, to rob and even to kill for food. It was not unknown for these little starvelings to carry pistols looted from some unwary American soldier; woe betide the man who, in the innumerable, noisome alleyways, fell foul of these infant predators who had more in common with the wolf pack than with children.

Rats, huge carnivorous creatures, also roamed the streets as desperately as did the humans; in their wake they brought diseases which spread with the rapidity of medieval plague and people died in their thousands. Medical teams worked the clock around to combat malaria, typhus, cholera, diphtheria, dysentery and venereal disease. The hypodermic needle was master; penicillin more sought after than gold. DDT Units operated in every street and people were sprayed whether they liked it or not.

Jimmy Erskine, Able Bodied Seaman, related a very amusing story. Minding the business of the big, bad, wicked world all about him he was walking near the docks and wearing LST rig, without a shirt, in khaki shorts, and with laceless boots, when suddenly he was pounced upon by a team of American Medical Orderlies; quite the biggest and ugliest bastards he had ever seen, claimed James; they thinking that he was of the people, quickly deloused the luckless matelot, whisked him into a mobile clinic where he was given a shot of penicillin in his backside, a shirt for his back and a parcel of food, and then sent packing, bewildered and bewailing his rotten luck. James was furious and the whole operation, he said, had taken about ten seconds flat.

The black market thrived, and the men who kept the market supplied were Allied servicemen. 'Deals' flourished in every bar and on every street corner. To leave a vehicle unattended was courting trouble; it was either stolen in its entirety or stripped to its axles; and as a result big American cars appeared on the streets after a quick 'paint job' driven by the bosses of the black market, not all of whom were Italian.

With the aftermath of Salerno and the subsequent build up for Anzio, Christmas, 1943, came and went almost without notice. A traditional lunch had highlighted an otherwise normal working day and the only man to get pie-eyed was the Chef.

In these months of the Italian landings Italy had not gone unnoticed; Jack, with his usual aplomb, had infiltrated, as and when the exigencies of Naval service permitted, in full measure. He insinuated himself into Capri, Sorrento and Pompeii, and, as the battlefield receded further to the north, into Rome itself.

To say that Pompeii had proved interesting would be an understatement of some magnitude; it had proved an unforgettable experience. The Professor, John Thomas and others of like mind, six in all, had taken the day off, and hitched a lift to the ancient city, transported thereto on the apron of a Sherman tank, courtesy of Uncle Sam; and they returned therefrom brandishing bottles of vino and singing songs of licentiousness and debauchery in a British army lorry.

At the entrance to the ruins they were met by the usual bevy of importunate guides; it seemed that even the war had not put them out of business; the Germans had proved to be avid 'culture vultures.' The sailors were offered an assortment of souvenirs which ranged from supposedly genuine Roman coins embedded in a lump of lava to picture postcards and pictorial guides to the ruins which were positively pornographic and touched up reproductions of the originals which adorn the walls of the ruins. The local *pièce de résistance* of the touristic offering was the 'Penis Ariolis' the flying penis, which was a small reproduction in metal of a mosaic motif which adorns the ruins; it was complete with wings, some had reins to assist the helmswoman to steer and all had an eyelet for attachment to a watch chain; it was to be worn, the guide said, as a lucky charm, a symbol of manhood and was guaranteed to amuse the ladies.

Because the currency was cigarettes or a tin of corned beef, all the party could afford a lump of lava, a guide book, a 'flying cock' and the price of employing a guide to show the party around the ruins. The sight of a party of American nurses, also bent upon the grand tour, assisted the sailors to resist the guide's suggestion that they dispose of their remaining cigarettes by a trip around the corner to visit a lady or two whom he knew; ladies, he assured them, who would be pleased to translate the poses of the Pompeiian mosaics into living reality and perhaps contribute a pose or two that even old Nero and his mates had not thought of.

The sailors told the guide that he was a dirty old man and his blandishments were further resisted when it was discovered that the nurses had a problem; they could not find a guide who was prepared to show them all the ruins, including the bits which feminine modesty should have forbidden them to see. Cigarettes succeeded where the nurses' beguilement had failed. The guide quibbled at a hundred cigarettes; that was starvation. He demurred at one hundred and fifty; after all a man had to live, but he settled at two hundred and he was chopping off an arm and a leg to do it at the price. The bargain struck and forces conjoined, sailors and nurses set off to do the ruins.

'This a housa is a how you saya a bachelori man's a housa. Two a mansa wotta dona getta marrieda si.' The guide sniggered.

'Homos,' grunted the nurses.

'Bleedin' brown 'atters,' said the sailors.

The original of the lucky charm, Penis Ariolis, four feet in length and carved deep in living stone, pointed the way to the Viale di Bordello, the Street of the Brothel. Inside the Lupanare the nurses gazed in silence at the faded mosaics upon the walls; illustrations of ancient, yet ageless, sexual activity, and they were not impressed. Jack studied the mosaics quizzically and with more or less purely academic interest; perhaps with the somewhat detached air of the connoisseur in such matters, and he, too, was not unduly impressed. The guide effaced himself, thus confirming the matelot's view that it was his own prudishness for which he was concerned and not that of the nurses. From the Lupanare the party emerged in thoughtful silence and not one dirty crack was made.

Another mosaic depicted a Roman legionnaire, or was he a centurion? Complete with steel helmet, breastplate, and raised 'kilt' he struck a vainglorious pose in a magnificent display of his manhood. In one hand he held a weighing scale; in the right balance was a bag of gold, whilst in the other reposed his penis; beneath the mosaic in Latin and translated into three languages for the benefit of the illiterate hoi polloi, was the legend:

'Worth its weight in gold.'

Once again the guide effaced himself. The sailors whistled through their teeth, the nurses gazed in silent appreciation, and thus the party stood *en tableau.* Suddenly one of the nurses laughed:

'Wal, goddamn,' she exclaimed; 'Ain't thet a lulu, – Ain't thet really a lulu?'

'Yeah,' retorted her sister-in-arms; 'thet shore is, – thet's a lotta cock!'

The ruins proved a place of enchantment; a place redolent of another age, an age more leisurely and more honest perhaps; an age without inhibition and prudery. They reeked of history, of a civilization which died with the Emperors; and now for a brief moment the city lived again in the imagination of the sailors and the nurses.

As well as Salerno, Anzio and all the other places on Italy's western seaboard, the LSTs also found time to liberate Corsica. They were the very first Allied ships to enter the port of Ajaccio since 1940 and great was their welcome. The bands played, the wine flowed, the ladies were charmingly accommodating to 'les liberateurs' and everyone trooped off dutifully to see where Napoleon was born. There was a lady who, in impeccable English, claimed to have been born down the Old Kent Road, said that she had done her bit for the resistance by running a brothel for the Germans; a brothel in which all her girls, as a prerequisite of their employment, were suffering from the pox. She and her establishment had wrought havoc amongst the enemy; 'but it is all right now, *mon cheri Anglais,* we have restaffed, *spécialement pour vous,* and the first screw is on the house!'

After Ajaccio, there was Bastia and the dreaded 'Bastia gauntlet' between Corsica and Elba to run. Here the dive bombers of the *Luftwaffe* appeared, but were beaten off by the escorts and never darkened the skies of the island again.

From Ajaccio to Gibraltar, to Southampton and then there were seven days, very welcome and hard-earned leave. Seven days were all there were to spare. During the previous few weeks the Allies had invaded Normandy, D-Day had gone down in history, Allied armies were fighting in France and the ship was needed to transport reinforcements to the beachheads. Before this could be done she needed a few minor repairs; hence the leave and Johnny Thomas and the Professor went home to Mum and Dad.

Chapter 12

Russian Convoy

'I was told the difficulties were insurmountable, or nearly so. My answer was: "as the thing is necessary to be done, the more difficulties, the more necessary to try to remove them".'
Vice Admiral Lord Nelson to HRH The Duke of Clarence. 7 April, 1803.

It was a changed Britain to which the men of the LSTs returned in the summer of 1944. Gone was the dread apprehension of the early war years; there was abroad a great spirit of friendship and of confidence in victory. There was also abroad a great industry, a mightiness of goings and comings and, pervading all, a great sense of being poised on the threshold of great events. History was in the making. Not the humdrum history of politicians, but the history of the impossible achieved and of a miracle in the performing; the history of a people's endeavour. This was a time when politicians counted for little; the people achieved despite them, not because of them.

Darkened cities pulsated with the tempo of fervent living, the forge hammered through the night and every night and there was an enthusiasm to see the war over and done with. Hitler's Europe would prove to be no pushover; that there would be hard and bitter fighting no one doubted; the road to Berlin would be paved with the nation's dead; but if that was the price to pay, so be it; the nation said let it be paid.

And the Professor and Gwen were getting married.

The lovers went to the altar married by special licence for the outlay of a few pounds in the church around the corner; he resplendent in his Number One Suit with a white ribbon to tie his silk, and she radiant in a dove-grey costume that had cost the family their clothing coupons for the rest of the war, and carrying a bouquet of freshly cut roses from Dad's garden. The ceremony was simple, the formalities were soon dispensed with and everyone went home to a party which lasted until the following morning; they all got drunk on war time beer, cider and American rye whisky. How the Americans became involved no one knew; when it was realized that they had brought the whisky, no one cared.

Gwen and her espoused saw little of the celebrations; early in the proceedings they slipped away to a small, first-floor front bedroom which had been placed at their disposal by a friend of Gwen's; here in a welter of passion they spent their honeymoon – the remaining four days of the Professor's leave.

The parting was poignant and tender; in her eyes, and rolling down her cheeks, were unrestrained tears. This was no brave wartime farewell as their last parting had been; this was heartbreak. In their hearts was a great and abiding love and also a great and abiding fear; fear of the sea and of the enemy above and below the sea. Their's was a love too precious to be sacrificed on the altar of senseless war. In his eyes there was a hot mist and in his heart a heaviness, an empty and growing dread. It was the thought of permanent parting which they feared. She went home to wait and he went back to his ship. 'Never mind, Prof,– Every time yew goes 'ome yew'll 'ave another 'oneymoon. Dirty, lucky bastard! No letter today, Prof – not to worry – pr'aps she's in the family way! Stop 'er bleedin' allotment, Prof– that'll make 'er write!'

From Southampton the LSTs carried the usual paraphernalia of war: troops, tanks, guns and trucks to support the army fighting its way into Fortress Europe. Troops and equipment for the trip to France; a hospital ship for the trip home. The tank deck had been fitted with triple rows of foldaway bunks, bolted to the bulkheads; six long rows of bunks were also fitted to the deck and on these a wounded man could be strapped in heavy weather. At the after end of the tank deck the wide-access platform had been fitted out as an operating theatre; and here beneath the glow of arc-lamps Naval Surgeons and teams of Sick Berth Attendants tended the wounded and succoured the dying. Also in attendance were two Padres: one Church of England and the other Church of Rome. The wounded were brought back from the battlefields to the beaches and loaded into the LSTs; the medical teams worked around the clock at the business of saving life; and on every trip buckets of severed flesh were consigned to the waters of the Channel. As the dead were not sailors, they were taken home for burial.

One poor wretch was brought back stark, raving mad and burnt half to death and yet he still lived. He was a Canadian, the sole survivor of a numerous body of his countrymen who had been captured by the Germans and herded together into a barbed-wire cage until it bulged from the sheer weight of their numbers; then a flame-thrower had been turned upon them. Men seethed with impotent rage and asked themselves what manner of barbarity it was that they fought.

There were many stories these days. Stories of women with their heads shaved, naked and hanged from the lampposts in the streets of the towns and villages of northern France. Stories of brothels set up in barns and such places where the amorous soldiery were knifed in the back by the women with whom they lay; women who had sold their souls to the devil and the Nazi cause. Stories base and vile. Stories also of bravery and sacrifice. Stories of men who had won the Victoria Cross, and of the French Maquis leader who had to stand by and watch his entire family shot in 'reprisal'. His was a choice no man should ever be called upon to make.

Trip followed trip until one day there were no more wounded and no more dead to take home for burial. Hospitals and graveyards had been established in France, and the LSTs carried prisoners of war instead. And a very dejected and disillusioned lot they were; all the spirit and defiance had left them; some were boys of no more than fifteen or sixteen years of age.

Back and forth shuttled the flat-bottomed ships, and then just before dawn one morning the Professor's ship struck a stray mine. There were heavy casualties, but the ship's company all survived to finish their journey to Southampton in a destroyer. There were few regrets at the parting from these strange ships; ships which did not even possess the saving grace of a name.

The Royal Naval Barracks, Devonport welcomed them in time-honoured fashion and with official compassion for the afflicted and sorely tried. A representative of those set in authority above the unblessed told them in manner which brooked no argument to 'Git yer 'air cut. Git shaved. Draw yerself a new kit. Angitbackyersharpish.' And 'gitbackyersharpish' they did, to be dispatched on fourteen days survivors' leave. 'Every leave a bleedin' 'oneymoon, Prof.'

Meanwhile the Consultant of the Oracle in the Drafting Office had decided to send Leading Seaman Walter Pater Martin, 'bleedin' hayfen' Smiff DSM, Royal Navy, otherwise known at home and in foreign parts as the Professor, to a brand new 'Castle' class corvette which was completing at a yard on the Firth of Forth. Able Seaman John Thomas, Royal Navy, was not detailed for this draft, so something had to be done and something was done. He appeared at the Drafting Office window, placed a tin of tickler on the sill, and asked in all sweetness and innocence, if, 'please sir and begging yer 'onour's grace' he could be sent to HMS *Brancaster Castle* with his friend Martin-Smith. For a brief moment the consultant said not a word, then the tin of tickler just sort of vanished; one moment it was there and the next moment, pouf, it was gone.

' 'Ang on a minit, son. Ah'll see. Do seem ta reck'lect as 'ow we wants a cuppla ABs fer 'er.' No sooner said than done; within the minute the consultant was back. 'Yer yar, me 'andsum; a draft chit ta wotsername – gityerbaganammick.' So it came to pass that the two friends in company with a full ship's company of some ninety-odd souls travelled north to join their new ship.

The company stood upon the dockside at Leith, Edinburgh, and, as the sun faded upon a beautiful day in the Indian summer of 1944, gazed upon the entity in steel and grey and white camouflage which was to be their home for some time to come.

HMS *Brancaster Castle* was a trim craft designed to stand on her nose, sit down upon her fat and robust bottom or lie down on her side in any weather which the world's oceans might throw at her. She had been designed and built as a long-range convoy escort, and her designers had used their genius to ensure that she lacked nothing in staying and striking power. Being the very latest thing off the stocks she was equipped with all the latest gadgetry for hunting and killing submarines and aircraft. For a comparatively small ship her complement of offensive weaponry was quite awesome. She was no ocean greyhound, but she was well found, sleek for a corvette, bigger than her sisters of the 'Flower' class and her accommodation was good. The remarks of her ship's company as they prepared to board her that first night, extolled her virtues: 'Christ, this bastard's no bigger'n one uv KG Five's (HMS King George V) sea boats!'

'Shagged if I'm lookin' forward t'goin' ta sea in this bleedin' tub. She looks as if she'll roll like a pig's orphan!'

By the time that she was ready for sea, trials completed and her company settled in, winter had come to Scotland. That country's northern extremities, ever a chilly place at the best of times, proved, to men accustomed to sunnier climes as Johnny Thomas and the Professor were, to be absolute anathema, and in the bitter cold they spent their lives both on and off watch huddled in their duffle coats. 'Nuff ta freeze the bollocks off a brass monkey.' Johnny Thomas summed it up admirably.

The ship cleared the Forth for the last time in a snowstorm. North about and through the Pentland Firth and the millrace of the Minches to Tobermory in the Western Isles, there to be inflicted with the dread 'evolutions' and to be worked up. 'I'd like ta work it up that fat ol' bastard's ass. I'd give the bleeder evolutions!' 'Darky' Davies, Able Seaman, had a very low opinion of the Admiral in charge of such matters who dreamt up those fearful impositions on poor long-suffering sailors; 'Darky' was by no means alone in expressing such an opinion.

In the bleak and blasting cold of the northern winter *Brancaster Castle* achieved a degree of efficiency, and great was the woe and lamentations which accompanied the achieving. In cold that chilled to the very bones, in sleet, rain, hail and snow, men bemoaned the allotted task and bewailed their fate, cursed their ' 'orrible luck' and longed for the warmth and friendship of the fleshpots of Leith and Auld Reekie (Edinburgh). 'Shakin' a wicked 'oof at the ol' Locarno Ballroom, a pint uv Willy Youngers' at any one of the hundred pubs which graced the road from the dockyard gates at Leith to the top of Princes Street; and of course there were the girls they had left behind, 'the puir wee lasses.' Everyone had left behind a girlfriend, even the Coxswain, 'dirty ol' git', for such was ever the fate of sailors. 'Roll on my bleedin' twelve!' (twelve-year engagement).

From Tobermory to Scapa Flow, 'not soddin' Scapa agin!' and Christmas was spent swinging around the buoy. Seasonal fare on the messdecks; turkey and Christmas 'duff' (pudding), carol singing and nostalgia, and strong men cried into their pint pots in the Fleet Canteen at Flotta on Boxing Day.

In January *Brancaster Castle* went to sea on her first convoy, on what was her maiden voyage as a fighting unit of the Fleet. She was designed for long-distance convoy work; she could cross the Atlantic, run down to Freetown in West Africa or run up to Russia without refuelling; and up to Russia she went, to Archangel, or, more precisely, to Polyarny on the Kola Inlet, the White Sea being frozen over at this time of year.

Since their beginning in the early days of the war the Russian convoys had been fraught with danger; hard fought, bitter affairs and dreaded by the men of the Navy. On the one hand the British Home Fleet and the convoy escorts: the destroyers, sloops, frigates and corvettes working far from their base. On the other hand the German High Seas Fleet: battleships, cruisers, destroyers and the ancillary U-Boats, E-Boats and minelayers, and ashore the feared *Luftwaffe* with their death-dealing dive and torpedo bombers working within only minutes' flying time from their bases; ships and aircraft worked as a tightly co-ordinated and deadly unit, and all with one, fixed intent, to stop the convoys getting through. To the north of the convoy route, close enough to throw stones at, the pack ice of the high Arctic; to the south the enemy-held coast of northern Norway, too far away to throw stones at, but too damned close for the health and well being of the sailors who would defy the blockade.

In these waters in winter a man stood little chance of being picked out of the sea alive. With temperatures down to thirty degrees below zero, in snowstorm or blinding hail, he would be dead almost as soon as he hit the water. And always the threat of the German fleet; always the threat of the dreaded Junkers and Focke-Wulfs which carried out around-the-clock dive bombing and torpedo attacks. For much of the year darkness brought no relief in this land-encircled sea of the midnight sun; for the remainder the attacks came under cover of almost total darkness, beloved of the E-Boats. The enemy had it all ways; and now in the early days of 1945 the convoys were fighting a desperate enemy with his back to the wall. Every ship laden with supplies which got through to Russia strengthened the Red steamroller which was forcing its way across Europe towards Berlin.

At the end of January, with dread in their guts and a prayer on their lips, the men of *Brancaster Castle* went to Stations for Leaving Harbour in a raging blizzard and, as she cleared Hvalfiord, the wind and the waves tossed the little ship around like a toy boat in a baby's bath; she pitched and rolled, shuddered, shook and shipped it green until it seemed that she must surely be engulfed; men thanked God that it was so; the storm would keep the enemy at bay, the battleships in harbour and the U-Boats well submerged. Snow piled high on the little corvette's deck, her rigging and superstructure froze and the waves and the wind sculpted the snow and ice into patterns until the whole ship was encrusted with fantastic white shapes and festoons of solid ice. On the upper deck, on the bridge and on the lookout positions men stood thigh deep in frozen snow; they were well protected with anorak suits, fur hoods, goggles, heavy leather seaboots and fur-lined mittens. All that could be seen of a man beneath his pile of protective clothing was the whites of his eyes showing vaguely through the smoked lenses of his goggles. The days of the duffle coat, balaclava and 'pusser's' navy blue scarf were long gone on the Arctic convoys. Their Lordships early discovered that it takes more than a duffle coat to keep a man alive in these conditions. If a man removed his goggles his eyes would freeze and if he touched naked steel with his bare hands the flesh would stick and peel off.

In such conditions the convoy formed up off Iceland's south-east coast. It was no easy matter marshalling the merchant ships and escorts in such weather, but marshalled they were and in pitch darkness they steamed to the north-east, to hug the icecap for much of the journey.

Life in the little corvette left much to be desired. Fittings broke loose and hurtled around the messdecks, tables collapsed and became lethal weapons, and hammocks, with their occupants fully clothed and muffled up for warmth because no one was allowed to undress at sea, swung to and fro with a mad, erratic motion. Men vomited indiscriminately where they lay or stood wishing to die, and wallowed in their own and others' spew. There were no cooked meals; everyone, from the Captain down, lived on corned beef sandwiches and tea brewed by the Chef at the risk of being scalded to death; when the bread ran out hardtack took its place. But with all her trials and tribulations *Brancaster Castle* was possessed of one major saving grace: she was bone dry. Her planners had done their job well; not a drop of water did she ship between her decks, and for that the small ship sailors of her company could forgive her many things.

For seven days and seven nights the storm raged and progress to the north-east was slow; the storm and the danger of floating ice had kept speed down. On the morning of the eighth day the weather abated, and with the dawn of the ninth day calm and tranquility returned to the northern ocean and with it came the imminence of attack.

In the few hours of semi-daylight permitted in these latitudes sea and sky could be seen as a vast uniformity of silvery grey; it was difficult to see where the sea left off and the sky began; the whole prospect was one of bitterly cold, brittle unreality. The ships, despite their Arctic camouflage, stood out in stark relief as they cleaved their way through a sea as calm and as flat as the surface of a mirror; only the great creaming 'Vs' of their bow waves and the peacock tails of their wakes relieved the scene of its 'toy ships on a mirror' quality. The total Arctic silence was uncanny; away to port the white immensity of Arctic snow showed as a slightly different shade of white between sea and sky, and the cold was such that it seemed that the quickened beating of men's hearts must surely freeze into stillness. Away to starboard the silver-grey of the ocean stretched to the horizon, and it was from that direction that the enemy would come. But no attack came, and for two more days and two more nights the ships pressed unmolested to the north-east. But in the ships there was no let up, no lack of vigil. The Chef cooked a great boiler of soup, or, more correctly, stew, because it was alleged to contain everything except the messdeck scrubbing brushes, and even their omission was a matter of conjecture; it was even rumoured to contain 'Tanky's' dirty socks and 'Jack Dusty's' yucky 'Y' fronts. But whatever it contained it was good and helped to revitalize flagging spirits.

The convoy altered course and, with a bearing on Bear Island, steered to the east and the tension mounted. Every knot now steamed took them that much nearer to the area of utmost danger; by the morning of the third day of calm, nerves were strained to cracking point, eyes strained into the half-light of the short day and with the ship closed up at action stations they waited for the inevitable.

'E-Boats bearing green six-o, Sir!'

The destroyers had already spotted the E-Boats and, with Aldis lamps flashing dispersal orders to the convoy, were turning to race and intercept. With the corvettes and frigates of the close escort to guard the flank the convoy turned to the north-east toward the pack ice, thus limiting the scope of an attack from port because of the limited space between them and the ice and, on the starboard side, putting the destroyers between them and the enemy. The big E-Boats skimmed the water, bouncing as they thundered in to the attack, the roar of their engines beating against the still, frosted air. Hull down, bow waves creaming, the destroyers sped to head them off. Flashes shot out from the destroyers' guns, and a few seconds later was heard the spiteful whap-whap of their 4.7s. Flashes too from the E-Boats as they took up the challenge and returned the fire. Thin, wavering streaks of tracer flickered and skeined out from the speeding enemy's close-range armament and raked the destroyers and, because the enemy was trying to work around the destroyers, the convoy turned again, stern on to the attackers. The E-Boats turned again, and the destroyers keeling over until their gunwales were awash, turned with them and headed them off once more. So was played out a grim game of high-speed checkers; move followed move with death and destruction for the badly placed. Attack and counter-attack, guns blazing and torpedoes running; a merchant ship erupted with a sickening roar and a sheet of flame: the all too familiar pattern of death upon the high seas. An E-Boat broke through the protective screen of destroyers and thundered down upon the convoy; as she came every gun that could be brought to bear opened up at her and *Brancaster Castle* fired her first shot in anger. Yet still she came and, astern of her, matching her speed knot for knot, and with guns belching pounded a pursuing destroyer. In a slithering high-speed turn the E-Boat came about and, in a classical attack at almost point-blank range, loosed off a torpedo at the nearest merchantman. Another sickening, belly-constricting crunch, another sky-leaping sheet of flame and another ship laden with tanks and supplies for the Russian front was ripped asunder and went to the bottom with all hands. As the E-Boat straightened out from her turn the pursuing destroyer hit her with her forward guns, blowing her conning position to kingdom come and reducing her upper deck to a shambles; yet still she thundered on at high speed, erratic and out of control, and again the destroyer hit her and she jerked to a standstill. The destroyer hit her again and with a roar and a sheet of flame she blew up. Other E-Boats died that day in the short Arctic twilight, and from the merchantmen and the E-Boats there were no survivors; their funeral tribute was a patch of debris-strewn and oil-fouled sea which after the action was as flat and motionless as an inland pond.

'Aircraft bearing green four-five, Sir!'

Over the horizon appeared the ominous black shapes of torpedo bombers, low flying and almost skimming the surface of the sea. The ships turned to the new menace and their guns blazed defiance; but it was the merchantmen that the enemy were after and they came on, hedgehopping the escorts as they singled out their targets. Attack followed attack by wave after wave of Focke-Wulf torpedo bombers which exacted a terrible toll; by the time that darkness returned another four merchantmen had found graves in the Arctic waste; again there were no survivors. It would have been a waste of time looking for them. No one could survive more than a few minutes in this cold. With the onset of full darkness the aircraft went home, but the E-Boats returned and the night was lit with star shells, the weaving crisscross streaks of tracer and the flash of gunfire. More blinding sheets of flame licked into the night sky and another two merchantmen sank. The battle raged well into the night until the E-Boats, ammunition spent, retired and returned to base.

But the convoy was not to be left in peace; the mode of attack changed; with early dawn came the first inkling that there were U-Boats in the area when another merchantman went up in flames. That was the tragedy of U-Boat hunting: invariably a ship had to be hit before the escorts knew they were there. Now it was the turn of the corvettes and frigates; fulfilling their role as submarine hunters they turned to the search. A bearing was taken on the stricken ship, the distance estimated and another thousand yards added and there ought to be your submarine. *Brancaster Castle* took up the tedious, dangerous business of the hunt. So many miles were steamed, yet so little was achieved. Submarines are as elusive as the fish with whom they consort. Pattern after pattern of depth-charges went over the stern, and over the bows, too, because she was fitted with a newfangled forward throwing device. But all the effort, all the miles steamed, all the bitter experience of the men exposed on deck, was in vain; no sign of U-Boats and another merchantman was sent to the bottom. While the U-Boats were hunted the ships also beat off the aircraft, and in the wings the E-Boats waited for their opportunity.

For three days and three nights the pattern of the action continued; torpedo bombers, E-Boats, U-Boats, and dive bombers were thrown into battle. In the British ships men muffled against the killing cold fought to retain a footing on decks made treacherous with ice, and the brittle unreality of the Arctic days and nights was riven by the sound of battle. Beards sprouted on ships' companies like the weeds in a neglected garden, hot meals were an occasional luxury and bodies began to smell.

Laden to the hatch coamings with tanks, guns, aircraft and supplies, twenty-six ships of the Merchant Navy had rendezvoused off the coast of Iceland; fifteen now remained. On the credit side, if there can be any credit in war, three E-Boats had been blown to pieces and two aircraft had been shot into the sea. So small the recompense; so great the sacrifice.

In *Brancaster Castle* the scene was the same as in all the other ships which fought the northern convoys through to Archangel. No one relaxed; work on deck, apart from chipping ice, was impossible; ship's companies ate when they could and slept when the enemy let them. There were no high spirits on the messdecks; there was nothing to get high-spirited about; in these high latitudes violence stalked abroad and death was a constant shipmate.

Sombre thoughts and fear ruled the messdecks in *Brancaster Castle* as she steamed towards Polyarny on that bitterly cold night in February. The watches had been changed from the 'first' (8 p.m. to midnight) to the 'middle' (midnight to 4 a.m.) and the Arctic night lay all about, pitch-black and brooding. Suddenly the whole forepart of the ship erupted with a shattering roar and a vivid sheet of flame. The Professor, Killick of the Watch on Deck who was returning to the bridge to report the Watch all correct, and who was abreast the funnel at the moment of impact, was slammed backwards against the after gun mounting shield with every ounce of breath forced from his lungs. Dazed, numbed with shock, only partially conscious and with a terrible pounding pain in his head, he fought for breath and awareness, not knowing where he was or what he was doing; in his mind there was a terrible conviction that he was dead, or at least dying.

This, he kept telling himself, is your lot, 'Prof' my boy, this is it, you've had it, this is what it is like to be killed in action. He was dead in the Arctic night.

So said a corner of his mind in this moment of shock. They would send a telegram to Gwen – that was a bloody funny thing to think about when you are dead. Then slowly he began to realize that he was not dead, dying or even injured. What miracle was this? He had seen the ship go up with a bleedin' great bang, right before his eyes. He was lying in a crumpled heap; as realization dawned he scrambled to his feet and stood swaying for a dizzy moment in a crazy lopsided ship. He realized that the deck was sloping at an alarming angle and listing to port and, as his faculties returned, he was engulfed by waves of nausea and he vomited. He peered about him, but in the almost total blackness of the night he could see nothing and, except for the lapping of the waves against the ship's side, could hear nothing.

He was standing thus, alone, and scared out of his wits when he heard a shout and saw a glimmer of light. It was the Captain's voice and what transpired to be the Captain's torch.

'Hello, there. Anyone alive there?'

Other voices called, torches were shining now as men answered their Captain's call and called to each other in the darkness; the Professor could see the red glimmer from the lights attached to men's Mae West lifebelts and he remembered to switch his on. A fat lot of good it would do if he was forced to take to the water. Men were gathering in a group on the sloping quarterdeck, holding on to the iron framework of the depth-charge throwers and shining torches into each others faces to identify those who still lived. Thank God it was mandatory to carry a torch at night. By the light of his torch the Captain was writing down names in his notebook.

Anyone whose name was not in the notebook must be dead. The Captain, Martin-Smith, a couple of Stokers, an Engine Room Artificer, Johnny Thomas, a Stoker Petty Officer, another couple of Able Seamen; all those who had been abaft the bridge when the ship was blown up. There were not many names for the Captain's notebook.

The ship had struck a mine; or was it a torpedo? In the absence of U-Boat contact and from the darkness of the night it was probably a mine; but there was no way of knowing. An unguarded light perhaps, a lucky shot in the dark? Whatever, *Brancaster Castle* had been blown in half; only the stern abaft the bridge floated still; and the Buffer (Chief Bos'un's Mate) reckoned that it was only the watertight for'ard bulkhead which was keeping what was left of the ship afloat: and from the ominous creakings and crackings which came from for'ard that might burst with the pressure and send the surviving half plunging to the bottom of the ocean at any moment.

An insistent hammering was coming from the forepart of the wreckage.

Someone was trapped down there, and the Captain called for volunteers to go down and see what could be done and to search for anyone else who might still be alive, knocked unconscious, lying wounded or trapped between decks.

The cause of the hammering was found to be the Sick Berth Attendant, trapped in the midships heads. 'Can't even 'ave a crap in peace – Ther' wus I, draws at the bleedin' dip, an' all uv a sudden, bang, and the whole bleedin' ship went up in smoke. That wus sum fart!' and the Chancre Bos'un chuckled with grim humour, thankful to be alive.

When the Captain was taking names and called the name of Thomas. J, a shipmate answered for him. Johnny was incapable of answering as he was lying jammed against the depth charge thrower, unconscious, with a broken arm and a fractured skull. A further two ABs were rescued from what was left of the after end of the for'ard messdeck, a small corner of which was still just above water and both were badly wounded. Of the rest of the foredecks there was nothing left, only the sea and below that the protective watertight bulkhead. Behind the bulkhead in the twisted mass of metal that had once been a boiler room, stores and a lower messdeck, came the sound of more hammering and of men who called desperately; but they had to be left; there was nothing which could be done as no man could get down there; they were beyond aid. Their's was the tragedy of unknown suffering, the substance of nightmare; they were the living who went to their deaths trapped in a tomb of steel, and their would-be rescuers returned to the quarter-deck heavy of heart.

The watertight bulkhead creaked and groaned alarmingly. The once proud ship settled deeper into the greedy sea; the situation was becoming critical and the wounded were made as comfortable as possible. Everyone huddled together for comfort and warmth and waited for rescue or death in the icy sea. Suddenly the night was pierced by the stabbing beam of a searchlight. The light probed the darkness until it rested on the stricken ship. Someone was taking an awful risk and the huddled group on the quarterdeck muttered a fervent 'Thank God.' Carefully the rescue ship nudged nearer, going astern; she dared not hurry the process in case she might disturb the wreckage and send it plunging to the bottom. From behind the searchlight a voice called, using a loud-hailer:

'Ship ahoy – ahoy there – ship ahoy!'

'Ship ahoy!' hailed the Captain of the *Brancaster Castle*.

'What ship?' enquired the loud-hailer.

The Captain told him, and the voice in the dark identified itself as the Captain of the 'Flower' class corvette *Bluebell*. He told the survivors that he could come no closer and was putting a boat over the side, and the light was switched off; risk enough had been taken already; even now they might be in the line of fire of a U-Boat attracted by the light. U-Boats were no respecters of rescue missions.

Came the light of torches and the splash of oars, voices and the survivors struggled with the wounded and clambered into the boat. Being a small boat from a small ship three trips were necessary, but eventually all were safe aboard the little corvette and she got under way and put distance between herself and the scene of the disaster, sweeping about to regain her station on the convoy which by now was miles away.

On the messdeck of *Bluebell,* in the crowded conditions which were the norm in the little ship, the survivors were made as comfortable as possible; every member of her company fussed around and tried to lend a helping hand and the wounded were tended by her Sick Berth Attendant and the Wardroom Steward.

' 'Ere yar oppo, have a fag.'

'Bar o' nutty (chocolate), mate?'

'Cuppa cha, chum?'

There was compassion in the little ship, and comradeship; normally she was overcrowded; corvettes always were, and now she was packed to capacity, bodies sprawled everywhere and there was scarcely room to move. The air was heavy with the stink of unwashed bodies and damp clothes, sweaty socks, cooking smells and the stench of oil fuel. Tobacco smoke hung in a blue pall over the bizarre scene; there was the heavenly scent of rum. From hammock nettles, overhead piping and various other 'stowages' hung festoons of clothing, drying dhobi-ing, steel helmets, gas masks, oilskins, rum fannies, mess kettles and anything else which might fly around in rough weather.

In *Bluebell* the Captain completed the notebook entries which he had started on the quarterdeck of his sinking ship. From a ship's company of ninety-eight officers and men only twenty ratings and one officer, the Captain, had survived. And now his ship was gone and no one had seen the going of her. She had gone, lonely and abandoned in the Arctic night, and she had taken her dead with her – and her living too. She had taken those who called out and those who screamed because they could not get out. There is no back door in a sinking ship. The Professor shuddered at the recollection and in his imagination he saw the dying moments of those trapped below decks in icy water; as the waters had risen men had cried to heaven and to their God for deliverance; they had fought and gasped for breath, gurgled and choked and fought again, but there was no deliverance; and the Professor cried, silently, as a man cries, and with a deep and abiding grief.

The late dawn of the high latitudes broke over a choppy sea and found the depleted convoy within sight of the north coast of Russia. The survivors of

Brancaster Castle were transferred to the light aircraft carrier *Nirvana* – a tricky operation in the rising sea. The wounded were taken below to the carrier's sickbay whilst the remainder stood on the carrier's weather deck to wave goodbye and God speed to their gallant little rescuer. Looking very small and insignificant from the height of the carrier's starboard entry-port she rolled and pitched her way to resume station on the convoy.

Suddenly a terrible sheet of flame shot skyward, followed a moment later by the roar of the explosion. A column of water fingered upward and bits of men and ship rained down upon the boiling sea; the rising wind blew the smoke away, the choppy sea resumed its normal aspect and a hushed and shocked silence fell upon the watchers in the carrier. Men gazed in mute horror; where there once had been a ship there was now no ship, just curving waves and a drift of smoke upon frosted air. *Bluebell* was no more. Twelve men out of ninety survived. That she had stopped a torpedo meant for *Nirvana* there was no doubt. The black-robed prelate of death and grief again stalked the decks of the ships which yet lived. Another name to add to the Roll of Honour; another name to add to all the other names.

Polyarny to starboard, Murmansk and Archangel just around the corner; but there was no welcome for the men and ships of the Royal Navy in this bleak and god-forsaken land. The merchant ships would unload as soon as possible and within a few days they and their escorts would begin the hell of the return journey to Iceland and Scapa Flow. 'No bright lights, no boozers, an' no parties (girls) 'ere Jack – this is Russia.'

Luckily, the return journey was made in some of the worst weather the northern ocean had known within living memory. *Nirvana* rolled as she had never rolled before. A flat top, a flight deck, had been placed atop an ex-passenger liner and this they called an aircraft carrier. This she undoubtably was, and in the dark days she served a very useful purpose, but a good sea boat she was not. Stability had been sacrificed to utility; she rolled abominably, she pitched, she tossed, she lurched and she cork-screwed; every time a wave hit her, and there were some massive waves on that run home, she shuddered from stem to stern. Those memorable seas swept her flight deck from bows to stern; the wind howled in screaming fury; hail, sleet and snow slashed down in horizontal sheets; her upperworks froze and her boats and standing rigging were carried away. Below decks all was chaos and hell let loose; fittings broke loose, lockers slithered all over the greasy decks from port side to starboard because there was nothing to stop them in the no-man's-land of her messdecks; tables capsized and joined the lockers in their murderous junketing; mess utensils became lethal weapons and collar bones and limbs were broken because everyone had the greatest difficulty in staying afoot.

And yet, because it was so, men rejoiced. The atrocious weather was an ally and the return convoy reached home without in any way being molested by the enemy.

In *Nirvana's* sick bay Johnny Thomas, with a turban bandage around his head and his arm in a plaster cast, was strapped into his cot in case he were to be pitched out and do himself another mischief. By his side, jammed between cot and bulkhead, sat the Professor. They spent most of their days thus: the Professor had no duties and his offer to help out with the wounded was gladly accepted by the Doctor.

'Won't be long now, Prof.'

'Coupla days, I reckon. Then we'll be home for another fourteen pen'orth of "survivors". Gets monotonous, don't it, all this leave?'

For a while they sat in silence.

'Wonder 'ow long this stinkin' war'll last, Prof?'

'Christ knows – looks like dragging on for ever.'

'Yeah.' Johnny mused a while, 'Wonder where they'll send us next.'

His friend laughed without mirth.

Chapter 13

Far East

'I pray we may have Peace, when it can be had with honour,'
Vice-Admiral Lord Nelson to Hercules Ross, Esquire.
12 September, 1801.

Johnny's home spread its arms in welcome; his plastered arm and turbanned head made him something of a local hero and to prove it he got sloshed once or twice, free of charge, in the local. The Professor and Gwen had eyes for no one but themselves, and were ecstatic in their oneness. But the leave, as all leaves did, sped to a conclusion. The parting was poignant, and all the family and most of their friends came to the station to wish the heroes farewell and hurry back.

In the barracks at Devonport life pursued its usual uniform round. Queues and yet more queues. Sweep the roads, sweep the canteen, clear up messdecks and flats for rounds, run with messages, fall in here, fall in there; fall in for breakfast, dinner, tea and supper; fall in to go ashore, go to the cinema, go to Aggie Weston's (Royal Sailors' Rest Homes), go to the pub and get drunk, screw the barmaid – if you were lucky – read, sleep and wait for a draft chit.

As the wheels of victory gathered momentum the Drafting Office crystal ball was plumbed nigh to the depths by the bloodshot eyes of the harassed Drafting Officer and his Delphic acolytes. What visions they conjured! What exotic places lay mirrored there in the crystalline depths! Far away places with strange-sounding names and most of them east of Suez. As ships were commissioned for the final assault on the empire of Hirohito there was great activity in the place of the destiny of matelots.

Shocking tales were told of the war in the Far East: the Burma Railway, the prisoner-of-war camps, kamikaze dive bombers with fanatical pilots who put their aircraft into a dive on target and forgot to pull out, Shintoism, hara-kiri and all that sort of thing. Not a healthy place was the land of the gentlemen with the slanting eyes.

Somewhere buried in the amorphous mass of King's Regulations and Admiralty Instructions, there was a section which dealt with the matter of survival at sea: 'and a man surviving one of His Majesty's ships of war shall, exigencies of the Service permitting, be granted six months shore service;

such service to include leave....' Or something like that. In the case of Johnny Thomas and the Professor the 'exigencies of the Service' did not permit their further retention in the land of their birth; they too had a draft chit and, said the Regulating Petty Officer whose nose peeped through the Drafting Office window, 'Don't quote KRs and AIs at me, sonny boy – Yew bleedin' lower deck lawyers is all the bloody same! Draft chit it sez 'ere, and a bleedin' draft chit you got – Gityerbaganammick.' And Johnny Thomas and the Professor without resort to bribery and corruption, joined their ship in Devonport dockyard; and she, in company with a fair sized portion of the British Fleet, steamed to the east.

HMS *Loch Garry* was a frigate and, as her name implied, of the 'Loch' class. Powerful and well versed in the affairs of war, she had recently been withdrawn from the Russian convoys and was a U-Boat killer with a hard-won reputation as such. Clean of line, compact and a comfortable good-living ship. She had been in commission a year from new, and had already put a DSO on the chest of the man who commanded her.

Johnny Thomas, now minus turban and plaster, and the 'learned one' joined her as reliefs for men who had either gone 'sick', developed symptoms of a compassionate nature, had pulled strings through friends in the right places or had otherwise decided that their talents could be better employed in places far healthier than the Far East.

Rain-lashed, with old Plymouth to port and Mount Edgcumbe to starboard, with a few tears and waves from 'heartbreak corner' and with Drake's Island fading into the mist, *Loch Garry* set course to the south and sunnier climes.

Gibraltar was still a boom town, and the 'rock apes' (the local inhabitants) yet waxed fat on Jack's predilection for hard liquor and bright lights.

Malta, despite acres of bomb damage, was making a valiant effort at getting back to normal. Grand Harbour was full of warships, and the bars of the 'Gut' and Floriana were full to overflowing with matelots on pleasure bent. The 'Gyppo Queen' (Egyptian Queen), 'The Galvanised Donkey' (The Golden Horse), and another hundred similarly named bars were back in business and the honky-tonks beat out their cacophony of noise until midnight each night.

Malta was taking up where it left off in 1940: 'Inside, Navy. Up top, Chief. We got big eats for da boys – steak, eggs, an' chips!' The 'ladies' of the cabaret were men dressed up, oh, so effectively, and one, known to a couple of generations of sailors as 'the Sparrow' was rumoured to be an ex-matelot. 'Feel 'is bum an' yew'll as like as not get a 'andful uv balls, whacker, an' 'e'll probly bounce one off ya. Right 'ard case that bleedin' 'Sparrer'!'

From Malta to the old stamping ground of Alexandria; through a placid sea and with a beautiful, blue and untroubled sky overhead and the air heady with the promise of the coming summer; through a sea where, not so long ago, the Royal Navy had fought such desperate battles; fought, indeed, for its very existence.

Victory in the desert had left Alexandria deflated. It was a city to which normality had returned; a ghastly normality of poverty, filth and crime. Gone was the prosperity which the desert war had brought; gone were the hundreds of thousands of sailors, soldiers and airmen who had sought relaxation in the teeming streets. It was now a city thrown back upon its own resources for its livelihood, and very slender those resources were. A greater poverty prevailed.

Steaming slowly through the Suez Canal the ship's company foregathered at the starboard rail and viewed life as it was lived thereabouts. On the banks of the canal the fellaheen of Egypt went about their mysterious affairs and the matelots sought entertainment: 'Shufty cush' they shouted to a grinning 'shit bint' (female fellah – Canal Zone variety); nothing loath the lady lifted her robe and with a black-toothed grin exhibited her sexual organs to the jeering sailors and, as an encore, turned about and presented them with a view of her bottom; a packet of cigarettes skimmed through the air to be caught dextrously by the grinning bint. Hard by a fellah also showed a wide black-toothed grin and with signs made it plain that he, too, would appreciate a packet of cigarettes; he lifted his robe and waved at the cheering sailors that part of the male anatomy which in polite society is normally deemed to be private. Cries of 'exeebish' were called from the ship; the gentleman fellah grabbed the lady fellah and pulled her to him, bent her over and, as Able Seaman 'Nutty' Bevan so succinctly put it: 'gave her a good, stiff talking to'. From the hands of an appreciative audience skimmed another couple of packets of cigarettes and the grinning fellaheen waved the ship a fond farewell as she steamed her way to the south and east.

The days grew hotter, and clothing became more scanty; birthday suits with lanyards and 'pusser's dirks' were accepted as normal rig, and all work ceased at seven bells each forenoon. A canvas bathing pool was rigged on the quarterdeck and the ship's company spent many a happy hour cavorting in the water like a lot of knobbly-kneed mermaids' boyfriends. But the further to the south and east they steamed the nearer grew the war and, although they cavorted and relaxed, the more the ship's company became preoccupied with their immediate future; as it topped the horizon each day the rising sun cast shadows long and potent with menace to the west.

Came a day, somewhere in the middle of the Indian Ocean, when the shadows lifted, if only for a brief moment; the sun shone brilliantly and the ship's company went delirious with joy. The war in Europe was over. Germany had surrendered. It was VE-Day. There were those who would celebrate and the King of England with the blessings of Their Lordships of Admiralty decreed that the Mainbrace should be spliced; the spirit of Nelson, resplendent in all its glory, stalked abroad at about four bells (six p.m.) in the second dogwatch. Two tots in one day! Glasses were raised high for the Loyal Toast and in some cases a little too high; the next toast was to peace: Peace in Our Time; 'Peace on earth and goodwill to all men – hic! An' fuck the bloody Japs!'

Colombo, indeed the whole of Ceylon, had been turned into a huge garrison, a springboard for the war in the east. The island teemed with servicemen and bars and restaurants did brisk business; after the austerity of Britain the shops and bazaars were a delight and a never-ending source of pleasure to the inveterate shoppers of the Royal Navy. Hand-carved elephants, sandalwood boxes, shawls from Kashmir, exotic perfumes and jewellery, ivories and a host of other things to embellish and adorn wives, sweethearts, mothers and mantelpieces. And, need it be said, there was a mountain of tea. Tea was rationed in Britain and there was tea to send home, at five shillings a pound, including postage and packing; right next to the tea stalls there was a prophylactic station staffed by the US Navy and open to all who would cleanse themselves of the possible consequences of carnal indulgence.

In the hills there was a rest camp for war-weary sailors; it being decided that the ship's company of *Loch Garry* were as weary of war as any other cross-section of the community, they were sent there for recuperation.

Kandy, their destination, proved to be delightful; a quiet and restful place, but this was not what Jack had come looking for. After the temples had been visited, Sacred Tooth and all, and due homage paid to the ancient gods, there was nothing to do and Jack spent a very frustrating week eating, sleeping, and basking in the sunshine. Service women there were aplenty, but these ladies were off limits to common, uncouth sailors. 'Strictly fer the hofficers, Jan boy!' Lord Louis Mountbatten came to say hallo, and the views over the jungle-clad hills were magnificent – 'but yew can't 'ave a bloody good run ashore on a view'; the matelots chafed for the bright lights of Colombo to which they gladly returned.

In Trincomalee *Loch Garry* met up with other units of the British East Indies Fleet: aircraft carriers, battleships, cruisers, destroyers and supply ships. Ships which had already done battle from the North Cape to the Falkland Islands, and from Matapan to the Java Sea. Now here they were, again poised for battle; to wreak a just and terrible retribution on behalf of the ships and their companies who now graced the bottom of these far seas.

One by one the Fleet put to sea, to form into battle formation as the harbour was cleared. East to the Straits of Malacca, the Celebes Sea, the China Sea and the Java Sea. East to where the war was still being fought and as the ships steamed into the rising sun there was dread in the hearts of their companies. These were the waters over which the kamikaze bombers flew, piloted by fanatics who went to their deaths rejoicing and thanking their gods and their ancestors for the privilege of being permitted to die gloriously.

Hard, bitter thoughts these sailors of the Eastern Fleet thought. To think that they had weathered the battles of the west only to come out here, halfway around the world, perhaps to die in these far-flung seas; their war, the war in Europe, was over and the nation rejoiced and danced in the streets. No one doubted that the Japanese, with their fanaticism and fatalism, would take a lot of beating. There was much hard fighting ahead; as a token gesture to the battles which lay ahead the Fleet was renamed the British Pacific Fleet.

The attacks, when they came, were of a ferocity that struck fear into the hearts of the men in the ships, and the massive barrages which met the attackers were on a scale never before witnessed by the veterans of the war in the west. The whole vast concourse of the United States Third Fleet, the British Pacific Fleet, the Combined Fleet Supply Train and their escorts, erupted like a great, lethal pincushion; tracer from a thousand guns skeined skywards, the air became filled with ack-ack puffballs, and the noise of the guns and the screaming whine of the diving bombers rose to a traumatic crescendo. Never was war fought on such a gigantic scale. This was no campaign being fought on a shoestring, as those in the west had been fought; here in the Pacific the whole might of the wealthiest nation on earth, with token support from her British allies, was being thrown into the final assault on the Japanese homeland.

Loch Garry and her consorts were left to escort the Fleet Supply Train and it was somewhere to the west of the Bonin Islands that *Loch Garry* experienced her last attack of the war. The ritual of the rum fanny had not long been observed and the ship's company was preparing to sit down to dinner when suddenly the action klaxon blared its warning and sent everyone scrambling madly to action stations. Out of the sun screamed the kamikaze bombers; up went the flak from the supply train and the day was made hideous with the noise of battle. The encounter was short and sharp, but it almost brought the end of *Loch Garry*. Moving into position to cover a large store ship she was singled out by the bombers and subjected to a heavy attack. The first aircraft of the diving formation was shot out of the sky; most of the others dropped their bombs and roared overhead, but the last of the wave must have been out of bombs and was bent upon suicide. Seemingly blessed with immunity she dived through the barrage of flak unscathed; on the ship men gazed in hypnotized horror at the plummeting aircraft but at the last moment the Captain ordered the helm hard over; almost at the same moment the aircraft was hit by the guns and plunging into the sea alongside she exploded in a sheet of flame and a mind-shattering roar which sent the little frigate reeling. Debris and flying metal screamed around the ship and she was badly blistered and dented in places, but the main damage was to her company; that evening, just before sunset, she buried her dead, and numbered amongst her dead was the Professor.

Johnny Thomas had only a few days previously been moved from number two on the port pom-pom to number one on the starboard; the funnel had been between him and the exploding dive bomber. When news of his friend's death was brought to him he went rigid with shock, was bereft of speech and for days afterwards went about in a daze of grief. For all the years of war there had always been him, his mate, the Professor and their ship. Now there was only him and his ship. The Professor was dead.

It seemed unbelievable. It was something to which he could not relate. Something good, a wonderful friendship, was gone from his life. During his every waking moment he half expected the elongated face with the permanently veed brow to appear amongst the living who milled around the rum fanny or who fell in part of ship. But such are the expectations of the bereaved. The Professor was dead.

That evening of the last attack, with the sky a translucent purple and the rising moon like a great, illuminated ball sending shafting beams of benevolence across the placid and shimmering sea, the ship's company of *Loch Garry* mustered amidships. Seven White Ensign-draped shapes lay on deck; at their head stood the Captain and all around, bare-headed and sorrowing, were grouped the friends and shipmates of those whose bodies were about to be committed to the deep:

We therefore commit their bodies to the deep...
according to the mighty working, whereby
He is able to subdue all things to Himself.

The Party piped the side, three volleys rang out, the mournful elegy of the Last Post was sounded and, as they turned forward to dismiss, the ship's company cried.

Four weeks later it was all over. The British Pacific Fleet went wild with joy. Ships' sirens blared exaltation, and men cheered and danced a jig of joy and relief; the clouds of fear were riven asunder by the sun rising without casting the shadow of death upon the sea; in celebration of the fact that the seas had been swept clean of the enemy and in common with every ship in the Royal Navy the world over, *Loch Garry* hoisted a broom to her masthead.

Japan had surrendered unconditionally. In one mighty stroke an empire had fallen and men talked in awe and with little understanding of Atomic bombs; bombs, it was said on the messdecks, which went off with a fucking great bang and laid whole cities to waste.

Once again on the day of a victory the spirit of Nelson stalked abroad, doubly enhanced by Royal Prerogative; Johnny Thomas got drunk, fell down a ladder and had to have four stitches put in his already sorely punished skull. A lasting memento of the day that peace and comparative sanity returned to the affairs of men.

In the weeks and months that followed the ships of the Eastern Fleet left station and went home, and great was the rejoicing. From Tokyo to Singapore and from Hong Kong to Colombo and Sydney the paying-off pendants fluttered and trailed long in the wake of departing ships. The bands played 'Rule Britannia' and the sailors cheered themselves silly; there were special cheers when the first shipload of ex-prisoners of war nosed out into Singapore Roads and headed west.

There were islands to clear of Japanese who did not know that the war was over, parades to celebrate ceremonial surrenders and hara-kiri was committed all over the Far East.

It was a happy time. A new kind of peace had been brought about. The Atomic Age had dawned, but when he arrived home Johnny Thomas had a widowed sister to face.

EPILOGUE

From September, 1939, when the first British warship, the aircraft carrier HMS *Courageous*, was sunk by a U-Boat with the loss of 518 lives, until 26 July, 1945, when the last loss was sustained with the sinking of the minesweeper, HMS *Vestal*, by a Japanese kamikaze suicide bomber for the loss of 20 lives, the Royal and Dominion Navies lost 356 ships of all classes from corvettes to aircraft carriers.

Amongst this total are not included submarines, trawlers which served under the White Ensign, motor torpedo boats, motor gunboats, motor launches, and landing craft of all descriptions; from the big Tank Landing Ships to Assault Landing Craft. If all such were included in the total it would amount to something nearer 600.

Listed here are some of the more tragic losses sustained by the Royal Navy only:

HMS *Asphodel.*	Corvette:	5 survivors from a ship's company of 90.
HMS *Avenger.*	Aircraft carrier:	12 from 555.
HMS *Bluebell.*	Corvette:	12 from 90.
HMS *Boadicea.*	Destroyer:	12 from 175.
HMS *Bramble.*	Minesweeper:	no survivors from 80.
HMS *Diamond.*	Destroyer:	lost with all hands together with some 300-350 soldiers whom she had just rescued from the sea.
HMS *Exmouth.*	Destroyer:	no survivors from 175.
HMS *Fleur de Lys.*	Corvette:	3 from 90.
HMS *Hood.*	Battleship:	3 from 1,350.
HMS *Kite.*	Sloop:	9 from 192.
HMS *Matabele.*	Destroyer:	2 from 200.
HMS *Neptune.*	Cruiser:	no survivors from 700.
HMS *Samphire.*	Corvette:	4 from 90.
HMS *Salvia.*	Corvette:	no survivors from 90.

These are only 14 of the ships lost; 62 men survived from ships' companies totalling 3,322. Nearly every ship lost through enemy action sustained casualties.

It was not unusual for men who had fought the early battles of the seas, and who had served in every theatre of war only to die fighting the Japanese in the Pacific five years later.

The war at sea cost the Royal Navy 50,758 men killed in action, 820 missing and presumed dead, and 14,663 wounded. Such was the price paid for the Navy's hard-won laurels.

If there be a life hereafter, Lord Horatio Nelson, though sorrowing for his darling children, must be proud of the men who served in his school.

AMEN